My TRUE *Story*

Standing
Alone

Jim Eldridge

For Lynne, for everything

Scholastic Children's Books
Euston House, 24 Eversholt Street,
London, NW1 1DB, UK

A division of Scholastic Ltd
London ~ New York ~ Toronto ~ Sydney ~ Auckland
Mexico City ~ New Delhi ~ Hong Kong

Published in the UK by Scholastic Ltd, 2011

ISBN 978 1407 11782 9

All rights reserved
Printed and bound by CPI Bookmarque, Croydon CR0 4TD

2 4 6 8 10 9 7 5 3 1

Jack Cornwell (full name John Travers Cornwell), Boy First Class, died aged sixteen. He was awarded a posthumous Victoria Cross (the highest British award for gallantry) for staying, seriously wounded, at his post as a sight setter for the gun crew at the forecastle of HMS *Chester* during the Battle of Jutland on 31 May 1916, while the rest of the gun crew were killed around him. He died of his wounds two days later.

PART 1

THE WAR ON THE HOME FRONT
LONDON 1914 – 1915

5th August 1914

My name's John Travers Cornwell, though everyone calls me Jack. I'm fourteen years old. Yesterday Britain declared War on Germany and my dad says he is going to volunteer and go and join the army and fight. My older brother Arthur says he's going to do the same. My dad says this isn't going to be just an ordinary war, like any we've had before, but a really big one, with the whole world caught up in it.

I was born on 8 January 1900 in Clyde Cottage, Clyde Place, in Leyton, Essex, during the last year of the reign of Queen Victoria. I was brought up in the country but in 1910 we moved to 10 Alverstone Road, Manor Park, Little Ilford, in East Ham, East London, which is where we live now.

My dad's name is Eli Cornwell. He's a tram driver. My ma's name is Lily. I've got three brothers – Ernest (who's two years older than me) and two younger brothers, George (who's a year younger), and Arthur Frederick. Ernest doesn't live at home with us. I've also got a younger sister called Lily, the same name as my ma. Lily is five years younger than me.

I have another brother and sister, but I suppose properly speaking they're my half-brother and half-sister as they're my dad's children by his first wife who died. My brother Arthur is 26 and works at a factory. My sister Alice is 24. To avoid confusion we call my younger brother, Arthur, by his second name, Fred.

When I was five years old I started school at Farmer Road School in Leyton, which wasn't very far from the house we lived in when we were in Essex. When we moved to Manor Park in London I went to Walton Road School. I stayed there until just before my fourteenth birthday, when I left to go to work for Brooke Bond & Co., a company that sells tea. My job is a van driver's boy, helping the van driver with his deliveries.

Soon after we moved to London, I joined the 11th East Ham Troop of the Boy Scouts, also known as the Little Ilford Troop, attached to St Mary's Mission, which is our local church. Our Scoutmaster is called Mr Avery. Now that war has been declared, Mr Avery says our troop are going to have to be dissolved, because all the Scout officers are going to join up and fight.

I really liked being in the Scouts because you learn so much about tying knots, and how to do so many things. I got my Tenderfoot Badge, and my Second Class and my Missions Badge. I also got a special Boy Scout Award because I saved a girl who was stuck in a drain, but my dad says that I shouldn't talk about it because I was just doing my duty and if I tell everyone about it that would be Boasting, which is not a good thing to do. My dad says that doing your duty and being respectful and honourable are the most important things in life.

My dad was a soldier before he became a tram driver. He fought in the wars in Egypt, and South Africa. Even though he is quite old, he says it is his duty to fight for the king and country, so he is going to join up in the army.

12th September 1914

Dad has enlisted as a private in the Home Service Battalion of the Essex Regiment, and he's gone to their garrison in Colchester. The home service garrison battalions are for men who've got a really bad illness or disability, which means they can't go off to the front and fight, or men who are older, like my dad who's 60. I know my dad wanted to go off to France and fight, like the old soldier he is, but I'm glad he's going to be in England. Colchester isn't that far away, and he'll be able to come home on leave now and then. Anyway, everyone seems to think the war will be over by Christmas, so he won't be away for too long.

The night before Dad left, he came out to our back yard, where I was sitting thinking about him going away. The army can be a hard life and Dad isn't a young man any more, and his health can be a bit doubtful, though he wouldn't like to hear me say so. He gets bronchitis when the winter comes, and he coughs really badly. I'd gone outside because I didn't want him to see I was worried about him, but he must have known.

"Having a quiet think, Jack?" he asked me.

"Yes and no," I answered with a smile.

He came and sat down next to me on the old wooden box I use as a seat.

"I ain't leavin' you with an easy heart, Jack," he said. "But this is duty. A man has to protect his family, and that's what I'm doin', joinin' up. Can you imagine what would happen if I didn't go, and no-one else did either?"

"The Hun would invade us, like they've done France," I replied.

"Exactly," nodded Dad. "And what would happen to you and your ma and all the rest of you if that happened?"

I fell silent, though I still felt an ache in my heart at the thought of him going, and being shot at. "I can't help worrying about you," I admitted at last. "If the Hun invade you'll be in the front line. It's going to be dangerous."

"It's dangerous wherever there's a war, son," he said,

and he put his arm on my shoulder. "None of us wants to go to war." And then he hugged me to him – something he hadn't done in years, and I felt tears welling up in my eyes, but I blinked hard so they wouldn't come. Dad had often told me it wasn't manly to cry.

"I want to come with you," I blurted out. "I want to join the army too."

Dad shook his head. "Sorry, Jack. You have to be eighteen to join up. You've got a long way to go yet."

"But there are boy soldiers," I said. "You went in as a boy."

"That was in the old days," said Dad. "Things have changed, and rules are rules. Anyway, you've got a very important job to do here. While I'm away, I want you to look after your ma and the rest of 'em. Arthur will be going out to France soon. But George and Fred will need a steadying hand. Someone to set an example."

"I'll do that, Dad," I assured him. "I promise."

"I know you will, son," he said. "You're a good boy, Jack."

He gave me another squeeze, then took his arm away. "I'll write to you, of course, when I get the chance. And I count on you to write back and let me know how things are going here at home. After all, your ma's not the greatest one at writing letters."

The truth was Ma couldn't read and write very well,

because she hadn't had much schooling. Dad hadn't had much schooling either, but he'd learned to read and write when he was in the army. That's one of the reasons he said the army was good for people like us. It gave us opportunities we'd never have otherwise.

Dad and I sat there for a bit longer in the yard, until the light began to fade.

"Time for me to go in," said Dad. "Your ma's packing my things. I've got an early start tomorrow." Then he went in.

I stayed there in the yard for a little while longer, thinking about him going off to war. I'll miss him.

15th September 1914

It's just been a couple of days since Dad left and went off to Colchester. Ma has been miserable, but she's trying to pretend to be cheerful. It didn't help that Arthur left today to join the army, though Arthur won't be going to France straight away. First he has to go and be trained as a soldier.

I told Ma I wanted to go and join up myself but, just like Dad, she says I'm too young. I don't agree with them. I've been thinking about it more and more since I had that talk with Dad in our yard, and the way I see it, if I'm old enough to go out to work and earn a living, like I do, then surely I'm old enough to go and fight for my king and country? After all, I know some boys and girls who are as good as married at the age of fourteen. I think it's unfair you have to be eighteen to join up and fight.

Afterwards, it struck me that perhaps the navy might let me join. Although you have to be eighteen to join the army, I know the navy have boys in it. They start as cadets and become sailors as they get older. We learned about the navy at the Scouts and at school. Britain has the greatest navy ever, and some of our greatest heroes were navy men. People like Admiral Lord Nelson, who defeated the French at Trafalgar, and Sir Francis Drake, who was the first Englishman to sail around the world, and he was a vice admiral in the fleet that defeated the Spanish Armada.

When I read about those great men, and how they went off in ships and did exciting things, I want to be like them. Lord Nelson was only twelve when he joined the navy, which is younger than I am!

16th September 1914

I went to the navy office to volunteer, but they told me fourteen is too young. They said I had to be sixteen to join. I thought about pretending to be two years older than I was. I know of some boys who got into the army this way. One boy in our street who is only thirteen joined up in the army by pretending to be eighteen, and they let him in! I can't believe the recruiting sergeant couldn't tell how young he was! But Dad says that I mustn't ever tell a lie. He says that lying causes all manner of bad things to happen to a person and will ruin their life and the lives of others, even if they do it for what they think is a good reason. Tell the truth at all times, says Dad, otherwise you are letting yourself down as a person and no one will trust you, because you will be known as a Liar.

I felt miserable because the navy wouldn't take me. After I left the recruiting office I went down to the Thames and looked at the boats there – big ones and little ones. Some were merchant ships, which go all over the world taking goods to distant countries and bringing other stuff back here. Some were passenger liners, which take people to far places like America and Africa. My Dad was in Africa with Lord Kitchener and has told me about it. It sounds like a really strange place, and very hot!

The ships I like best are the navy ships. In the old days, which is not really so long ago, the navy ships were made of wood and their weapons were cannons. Now they're made of metal and instead of cannons they have huge guns on them which can fire shells for miles!

I watch these ships sail up and down the river and look at the sailors at work on the decks, and I wish I was with them. I want to be a gunner, firing shells at the Hun and sinking German battleships. I wish I could join the navy now and get into the action! I don't want to have to wait another two years – the war could be over before then!

4th October 1914

Today we got a letter from Dad! He sent two letters, one to me and one to Ma. In my letter he asked me to help Ma read his letter to her.

Dad didn't say a lot about what he's doing because he says that if you put too much information in a letter and it falls into enemy hands, they can work things out – like where your regiment is, how big it is and what morale is like. Dad's letter was quite cheerful.

Dear Jack

Well, here I am in Colchester, serving once more under Lord Kitchener. It's not really the same as before, because then he was a field general and he led us troops in battle. Now he's doing an even more important job as Secretary of State for War, running the whole thing, and there couldn't be a better man for the job. He was a great general, the best I ever served under, and he's still a good 'un! If all our generals were like Kitchener, we'd have the Hun licked in double-quick time!

Things here aren't bad. The food could be better, but then it is army food, and I've got used to the food your ma makes. There's no better cook than your ma, and her puddings could make any man happy, especially her bread pudding. I wish you could send some out, but I suppose it could get lost on the way.

I had an aunt who used to make bread pudding, but hers was as hard as a brick. We could use it right now to fire at the Germans from our big guns in France.

As you can tell, I'm in good spirits. Give your ma a hug from me, and tell George, Fred, Lily and Alice that I'm thinking of them. Tell them to keep their chins up. And that goes for you too, Jack. We have God on our side and we will win!

I remain your loving
Dad

He didn't mention Ernest. Like I say, Ernest doesn't live at home. There was a sort of falling out between Dad and Ernest last year, and Ernest went off, and we haven't seen him since. I don't know what he's doing. It's strange having a brother you never see, or even know about. I thought of asking Ma if she knows where Ernest is. I did ask her about six months ago, before Dad went off to join up, but all she said was "Don't mention Ernest. It only upsets your Dad." I never found out what the upset between them was. And Ma won't say.

6th October 1914

A lot of people said that when the war started it would all be over in a few weeks, or by Christmas at the latest. It's now been going on for two months and it doesn't look like it's going to be finished any time soon.

Ma worries a lot about Dad because of his health, especially his bronchitis.

I'm still not exactly clear on what this war is all about. I asked Dad just before he went off to Colchester, and he just said that it wasn't up to us ordinary people to get involved in the whys and wheres of things. It was our duty to support our king. So I asked Arthur before he went, and he told me what he knew about it.

According to Arthur, the war's happened because of treaties between countries, which means one country signs a contract with another country to say they will be friends and allies, and if anyone else attacks them then they will join together. It seems we have a contract like that with Belgium, and Germany has a contract with Austria-Hungary, and Serbia has a contract with Russia. I'm not sure who France has a contract with. I think it might be Belgium. Arthur thinks France had an agreement with Russia.

Anyway, it all started in June this year when some Duke called Archduke Franz Ferdinand was killed by an assassin. Arthur says this assassin was either a Serbian or a Bosnian, he wasn't sure which. Whichever he was, Archduke Ferdinand was Austro-Hungarian; so the Austro-Hungarians declared war on the Serbians because of this assassination and attacked Serbia. Because the Serbians had an agreement with Russia, Russia came into the war on the Serbian side. Germany had a contract with Austria-Hungary, so they declared war on Russia. And because Russia and France had an agreement it meant Germany also declared war on France.

Then the Germans invaded France, and because France and Belgium are right next to one another, they invaded

Belgium at the same time. This meant that Britain had to declare war on Germany and come in and defend Belgium, as well as France. At least, that's what Arthur said.

I must admit, it all seems a bit confusing to me, which is why I think Dad's way is best – don't ask questions, just do your duty.

15th October 1914

Today we had a letter from Arthur. He has finished his training and is off to France. His letter wasn't very long, but he said that he would write more once he got to France. I'm not sure if he will because Arthur doesn't like writing letters, but we'll see.

I wrote a letter to Dad today telling how things are here, and how we are thinking about him. But I didn't put in too much of that. Dad doesn't go in for being too emotional. He says that the thing that makes us British and better than anyone else is the fact we don't go to pieces when things aren't going our way. He calls it having "a stiff upper lip". I think that means that when bad things happen, you mustn't cry, you just get on with things. Mind you, although he says that, I remember him giving me that hug the night before he went off to Colchester, and I realized that underneath all the things he says, he cares a lot.

4th November 1914

Yesterday the German navy attacked Great Yarmouth on the east coast. A German battlecruiser sailed right near to the coast and started shelling the town. The papers didn't say if anyone was killed, just that there was lots of damage. I'm shocked by this. I don't understand why our navy ships didn't go out and fight the Germans and attack them and sink their ships, though I didn't say it out loud to anyone because it could be *treason* if you criticize your own side.

Our neighbour, Mr Adams, who is too old to go to war, says our ships couldn't get out because the Germans had put mines in the sea. These are bombs that float just beneath the surface of the water and they blow up if anything touches them. Mr Adams says the Germans know where they have put their mines and that's why the German ships don't get blown up by them. I said that surely these mines would just float, and so any ship could hit it, but Mr Adams says the Germans weigh their mines down so they stay in the same place.

Mr Adams says that a lot of our ships are fighting the Germans in other parts of the world, and we need them back if we are to defend our coast from the German navy.

6th November 1914

We have had a letter from Arthur. He says it's very wet at the front, on account of all the rain, and the trenches the soldiers live in can get filled up with water. But he tells us he's keeping fine on the whole and not to worry.

I read his letter to Ma, but I can tell she doesn't believe that everything's all right. She spends a lot of the time trying to find out from other people any news they have from their men at the front to find out what's happening. She says this war is going on a long time. I know that she is worried that the longer the fighting goes on, the more chance there is of Arthur getting wounded. There have already been quite a few families in our street whose sons or fathers have been killed or injured in the fighting. She's also worried because there are stories that the soldiers spend most of the time soaked through in the trenches. I'm glad Dad isn't in the trenches, because with his bronchitis that could kill him.

One of our neighbours, Mrs Sims, says her son Henry has caught lice out there. And not just little lice in his hair either, like everyone gets, but really big lice that crawl all over his body. She also claims that Henry has seen rats in the trenches as big as cats, but I'm not sure about that. Henry was always exaggerating things when he was at home.

1st December 1914

Judging from the stories in the newspapers, the war is spreading right over the world. What Arthur said about different countries having contracts with other countries is bigger than I realized. I know that Australia, Canada, New Zealand, India, and lots of bits of Africa, like South Africa, are all part of the British Empire and so are our allies in this war. But Germany also owns parts of Africa, and so do countries like France and Portugal, and all these other countries are coming into the war on the side of their mother country. So there is also fighting going on in Africa and around the Mediterranean.

I got out my atlas, which I won as a prize at school for

doing good work, and looked up all these different places to find out where they were.

9th December 1914

Dad came home on leave today. It was really great to see him again. He cut a fine figure in his uniform, and lots of the neighbours came round to see him to ask about the war. Dad says they do a lot of training and practising, and they are very busy building defences around the coast. To be honest, I was surprised at how fit he looks, considering his age. I think being in the army must be good for him.

He only stayed for two days, then he had to go back to Colchester. He said he won't be able to get home for Christmas. It will be strange to have Christmas without Dad here, but, as he said, a man has to do his duty.

13th December 1914

I've changed my job. I left Brooke Bond and I've gone to work as a dray boy with the Whitbread brewery at their depot in Manor Park. The dray is a large, open-sided cart pulled by two horses, and it takes the barrels of beer from the brewery to the pubs. My job is to ride along with the driver and help him to unload the barrels of beer and collect the empty barrels.

I get better wages at Whitbread than I did at Brooke Bond. Working on a dray will make me stronger because it is heavier work, which will help when I join the Navy. I'm determined to join up and play my part in this war. It's what Dad would want, and if I can't get into the army until I'm eighteen, then it's the navy for me.

My driver on the dray cart is a man called Jebediah, though everyone calls him Jeb. He's a nice enough man, but a bit grumpy. He also wheezes all the time when he talks, and even when he doesn't talk. I think he has something wrong with his chest – a disease, or something. Jeb's wheezing is even worse than Dad's when he has his bronchitis. Lots of people in the East End of London have chest diseases because of the damp and smoke from all the chimneys.

Me and Jeb talked about the war as we drove around delivering our barrels of beer. He said he thought it was strange that we were at war with Germany.

"Why?" I asked.

"Because our king and their king – though they call him the Kaiser – are the same family."

"You mean their king's English?" I asked, puzzled.

"He's half English," he said. "You know the old queen's husband was German?"

"Of course I do," I nodded. "Prince Albert the German."

"Well there you are, then," said Jeb. "Their king is half English and our king is half German. First cousins and such. You can tell because even their name is German."

"Whose?"

"Our king and queen. King George and Queen Mary. Their name is Saxe-Coburg-Gotha. You can't get more German than that." He shook his head. "I always thought the next war would be against the French. It usually is."

14th December 1914

There was a row today between Ma and my big sister,
Alice. It wasn't a big row, because Ma doesn't do big
rows – she likes a quiet life. It's noticeable that since Dad
went off to join up and isn't at home, Alice speaks out
more, speaking her mind. Today she was talking about
votes for women. Before the war started there was a
campaign by a group of women called Suffragettes to
give women the right to vote in elections. Most of these
women were very posh and they held meetings in the West
End and other places. They're led by a woman called Mrs
Pankhurst. When the war started, Mrs Pankhurst said that
women should stop pushing to get the vote but should
put all their energy into the war effort and get behind the
soldiers fighting at the front. Now it seems that one of this
Mrs Pankhurst's daughters has come out and said that her
mother is wrong and that this is the time for women to
fight for the vote, and she is going to start up her campaign
here in the East End. Alice said she thought that was a good
thing. Ma said she didn't want the vote. She thinks politics
and running the country are men's work. Alice blew up

and said that women worked just as hard as men and had just as much right to say who ran the country as men did. Then Ma got all tearful and said it was wrong of Alice to talk like that when the menfolk were out risking their lives fighting the war.

When Alice saw that Ma was upset, she calmed down a bit because no one likes to see Ma upset, and we all know how worried she is about Dad and Arthur. But Alice still said she hoped that the politicians would do the right thing and give women the vote.

Me, I don't know what the right and wrong of this is. When there were all these meetings and protests before the war, with some of the suffragettes going to prison because of the things they did, like breaking the windows of government offices, Dad said they all ought to be locked up. He said that women didn't need the vote because the men would vote on their behalf. When he said things like that, Alice went all quiet and gave him funny looks, but she didn't go for him like she did Ma today.

15th December 1914

There are reports in the papers saying that our navy destroyed the German fleet in the South Atlantic, off the Falkland Islands. I have looked up the Falkland Islands in my atlas. They are small islands off the eastern coast of South America. This victory is great news! The battle was over a week ago, but news takes a long time to get back to us when things happen so far away.

18th December 1914

The German navy launched another attack on some English towns on the north-east coast! This time German battlecruisers came right up to the coast and fired shells on Scarborough, Hartlepool and Whitby. Eighteen people were killed, all civilians.

The newspapers are asking how these German ships were able to get past the Royal Navy ships in the North Sea to make this attack. It seems lots of people are blaming our navy for not defending the coast properly, but I am sure there is more to it than this. Our navy does its best, but many people say that the German battleships are faster than our ships, which is why we can't catch them. I think that people who say this sort of thing are *traitors*. We should be praising our navy and helping them defeat the Hun, not criticizing them. Also, most of our navy has been in the South Atlantic where they have sunk the German navy. I'm sure those ships will be able to come back and defend our shores.

25th December 1914

Christmas Day. It should have been a happy time, but as we sat around the table and ate our Christmas dinner and toasted one another's good health, all I could think of was Dad at the barracks in Colchester and Arthur in the trenches. I really do miss them both. I wish they were home with us.

I know Ma feels the same. We put out two empty chairs at the table, one for Dad and one for Arthur, and I caught her casting unhappy looks at them when she thought no one was looking.

Alice is a young woman with her own life, and although she says she worries about Dad, I don't feel she misses him like I do. I think she is more worried about Arthur. That's understandable, because Arthur is her proper brother and only two years older than her. Alice sticks by Dad's saying about keeping a stiff upper lip, and not letting her feelings show.

The ones I have to keep an eye on are young George and Fred. Since Dad went off, they can be a bit of a handful. Ma can't keep them in check as she should, so I told them that if they don't behave I'll write to Dad and tell him what they've been up to, and he'll get angry with them and have a go at them when he gets back. That usually sorts them out because Dad can have a bit of a temper, especially if he thinks anyone is being disrespectful to Ma.

8th January 1915

My birthday. I am now fifteen years old. One year nearer to being able to join the navy. This is my first birthday without hearing Dad say to me, "Happy birthday, Jack." It feels strange and lonely without him. But I shall do what he says, which is *my duty*.

20th January 1915

There was another attack on Great Yarmouth yesterday, but this time it was from the air! A zeppelin flew across from Germany and dropped bombs on the town and the coast. The army tried to shoot the zeppelin down but I imagine their shells couldn't reach it.

I saw a picture of a zeppelin in the paper. They're like huge, long sausage-shaped balloons filled with air, and the pilot and the crew sit in a kind of carriage underneath it.

I've heard that some of them have been shot down by pilots from the Royal Flying Corps. When the bullets hit a zeppelin they catch fire and blow up because of the kind of gas they use inside the balloon. I suppose there were none of our planes near Great Yarmouth when this zeppelin attacked.

3rd February 1915

I talked to Jeb today about wanting to join up and fight, and he got moody when I said this.

"It's all very well fighting for your king and country," he said. "Trouble is, no one cares about you when the fighting's finished and you come back home." He patted his chest. "I got wounded when I was in the army. I lost nearly all of one lung. No one cared. Not the army, nor the government. They just kicked me out and told me to fend for myself."

"Where were you?" I asked.

"South Africa," said Jeb. "The Boer War."

"My Dad was in Africa," I told him. "He fought with Kitchener. He's with the Essex Regiment now, but in England, defending. He joined up as soon as war was declared."

"I tried to join up," said Jeb. "When war was declared, I went down to the recruiting office, despite what had happened to me, and said I wanted to go and fight. But they wouldn't have me because of my lung." He gave a big heavy sigh, which made his wheezing even worse. "I should be fighting, not driving a horse and cart."

20 February 1915

The Hun are attacking our ships with their submarines. They sneak up on a ship and fire torpedoes at it. The people on board the ship don't have a chance! Our navy is doing its best to try and track down the German submarines and sink them. The sooner I can join the navy and play my part, the better!

24th February 1915

Today something terrible happened to me and Jeb while we were on our rounds. We had stopped outside a pub and were unloading our barrels when a lady came up to Jeb. She was all dressed up in good clothes, and spoke posh. She looked at Jeb like he was something horrible and said, "A man of your age should be in uniform, fighting at the front!" Then she produced this white feather from her bag and held it out to him. Giving a white feather to someone is a sign that they are a coward.

I stood looking at the white feather and at Jeb, and I felt shocked. Jeb is no coward. Jeb glared at the woman, snatched the feather from her, scrunched it up in his fist, threw it on the ground and trod on it.

He snapped at her. "I did my bit for my country and I lost a lung because of it! Go and give a feather to your husband, if you've got one!"

With that he turned his back on her and carried on unloading the barrels. For a moment I thought the woman was going to hit him with her brolly, but then she just turned and walked off.

Jeb was really angry, and for the rest of the day he sat next to me glaring at the horse as it pulled the cart along, not saying a word, but I could tell how furious he was.

"She didn't know you've only got one lung," I said trying to make him feel better.

"She don't know and she don't care!" Jeb said angrily, and he spat down towards the cobbled road.

What I didn't say out loud was that I was worried that someone was going to give me a white feather too. What would I do if that happened? I would know I was too young, and that I'd tried to join up but had been turned down. But some people say I look older than my age. Even though it would be unfair, I don't think I could stand the shame. It's the same for Jeb. It's not his fault he's not in uniform, but I could tell that he felt angry at what had happened, and ashamed.

6th March 1915

There was another row today between Ma and Alice. Alice said that the government was going to turn the old caustic soda factory in Silvertown into a munitions factory, making gunpowder and shells and bullets. A friend of hers called Theresa said she was going for a job there because she'd be paid 25 shillings a week! Alice said she was thinking of going for a job at the factory with Theresa but Ma didn't look happy about it.

"That's not a good place to work," she said. "Making munitions is men's work really. I've heard about those places. Only rough women work there."

At this Alice got upset. "Are you saying that Theresa's rough?" she demanded angrily. "I've known Theresa ages and she's a good girl. Her husband, Bert, is away fighting in France, just like Arthur. She says she's going to do it because our troops need shells and ammunition, if we're going to win this war. She's doing it for her Bert and

Arthur, and all the rest of our boys out there."

Alice's anger made Ma back off. I don't think Ma was expecting Alice to be so upset. After all, she was only saying what lots of other people were saying. I'd heard some of the men at the brewery talking about the women who were doing men's work, like a job in a munitions factory, and how the women who worked there were a bad lot, more like men in the way they acted – swearing and spitting and everything.

"I'm not saying your friend is rough," said Ma. "I'm just saying that the work is rough. Filling shell cases with gunpowder. It's dangerous. Something could blow up and you could get killed."

"Arthur could get killed fighting in France," argued Alice. "That's why they need shells and ammunition."

Ma fell silent, then said: "Well, the factory's not open yet, so I'll write to your dad and see what he says about it."

That shut Alice up, because she knew that Dad would feel the same as Ma. Dad's old-fashioned that way. So instead Alice said, "No need. I'll write to him myself." But I knew she wouldn't.

9th March 1915

I told Jeb about the row between my ma and Alice, and how the women at Silvertown were going to be paid 25 shillings a week. He told me about a niece of his who works at a munitions factory in Kent. "They may get paid well, but they work hard for it," he explained. "I went down to see my niece one Sunday a couple of weeks ago. She was all yellow."

"Yellow?" I said, completely confused.

Jeb nodded. "It's from the powder they use to make the TNT," he told me. "It gets in their skin and no matter how often they wash it stays there. Mary, that's my niece, says she washes all over when she gets in from the factory and the water turns this sort of blood-red with the chemicals, and her skin is left yellow. Even her toenails have turned yellow. Mary says she's luckier than most. Some of the women have developed skin rashes because of the chemicals."

I thought, I've got to tell Alice about how she's going to be turning yellow if she goes to work at the munitions factory. Then I thought I wouldn't, because if I did she might get mad and say I was siding with Ma against her.

25th April 1915

The war goes on. The letters we get from Arthur suggest that both sides are stuck in the same place, not able to advance. Sometimes our side makes an advance and the Germans are pushed back, then a short while later the Germans attack and push our men back. And they are back on the same piece of land they were on before, but lots of men have died.

I really want to be out there, helping Britain win this war.

There are reports in the papers that the Germans have been using gas against the troops. Arthur didn't say anything about gas in his letters. Someone said the Germans had used the gas against the French troops, which is why none of our soldiers know anything about it. I hope Arthur doesn't get gassed.

9th May 1915

A German submarine has sunk a passenger liner, the *Lusitania* with torpedoes. The newspapers are calling it one of the most cowardly acts of the war, because the ship wasn't a warship of any kind, but a liner sailing from New York, in America, to Britain with nearly two thousand ordinary civilian passengers on board. The German submarine attacked the *Lusitania* when it was passing the coast of Kinsale in Ireland.

It makes me so angry when I read about things like this. It's bad enough that soldiers and sailors and airmen are dying in this war, but they are in combat and know what they are doing, and they know that being killed or wounded is a chance they take. But the people who died when the liner was torpedoed and sunk were just ordinary people.

Apparently the German submarine didn't give the ship's passengers on the ship any chance to get into the lifeboats after the first torpedo struck, because they fired a second torpedo immediately after, and the ship went straight down. Some people managed to survive, but over a thousand people died when the ship was hit and sank.

This has made me even more determined to join the navy and go to sea, and seek out these submarines, and the rest of the German navy, and sink them!

16th May 1915

Yesterday Jeb and I were delivering barrels of beer to a pub next to Charing Cross railway station, and we saw all these wounded soldiers being put in buses and coaches. There were hundreds and hundreds of them. Some had legs missing. Some had arms missing. Some had bandages wrapped round their heads. Some were blind and were being led along in a line, holding on to the back of the man in front. I'd heard people talk about the soldiers coming back wounded, and I'd seen lots of them in our neighbourhood, but I'd never seen so many injured soldiers in one place before.

"They're the lucky ones," said Jeb. "The unlucky ones are lying dead back there in France."

"They're not lucky," I said. I pointed at the line of blind soldiers making their way towards one of the waiting coaches. "What are they going to do now?"

"Beg," said Jeb. "But at least they're alive."

As we drove the cart away, I looked back. More wounded soldiers were pouring out of the station, and more buses and coaches were pulling up to collect them. All I could think of was Arthur and I prayed that he wouldn't come back like that.

1st June 1915

Last night there was a zeppelin attack on London.Lots of people were killed and buildings destroyed. People are getting worried. They say that if the zeppelins can drop bombs on London, then they can drop gas on us as well.

It seems that we're under attack from all sides. The German navy is shelling our coastal towns, and the German zeppelins are dropping bombs on our towns and cities inland. I have to do something more than just driving around with Jeb delivering barrels of beer. What I do isn't going to win this war. It's been going on for nearly a year and it still looks no nearer to being won.

3rd June 1915

I talked again to Jeb today about joining the navy. He said I should lie about my age. He said I'd get away with it because I look older than I am, but I told him what Dad had drilled into me about not lying. Jeb suggested I try again, and keep trying until they let me in. The trouble is, I worry that if I keep on trying and they keep sending me away, it'll count against me and the recruiting officer will just automatically turn me down when he sees me come in again. I've got to be clever about this and think about what I can say to persuade the navy to let me in when I next go there.

15th July 1915

This afternoon I went to the Royal Navy office again to volunteer, and this time they said I could join! I reckon because of the war they must have relaxed the rules.

The trouble was, they said that because I was only fifteen I needed my father's written permission. I told the recruiting officer that my father was away in the army, so it wasn't easy for me to get written permission from him. This was only a white lie – I could write to Dad and ask him to give his permission, but I was worried he might think I was still too young.

The officer said that if I could take him letters proving my good character from responsible adults, such as the headmaster of my old school and my employer, then that should do the trick and I could enlist and start training as a boy cadet. So I will be able to join the Navy after all without waiting!

I came home and told Ma and George and Fred and Lily. George and Fred were really jealous and said they also wanted to go and join up, too. Ma told them they were both too young. She said that she would have a husband and two sons away fighting and she needed them both at home to take care of things.

Lily got upset and hugged me, and said she was worried I'd get shot and wounded. Someone had told her that the son of a family down the road had gone to France and been killed and she was already worried that the same would happen to Arthur.

I told her not to worry, that I would be in the navy. The navy was different from the army because you were on a ship, which meant the enemy were always far away, and couldn't creep up on you and shoot you. You could see them coming across the sea. George said you wouldn't be able to see them if it was night time, and that upset Lily who started crying and saying I'd be killed. So Ma told George off, and said that I had to do what I had to do. That I was going to protect them and everyone else, and they should be proud of me.

27th July 1915

Today I joined the navy! I am now Naval Cadet John Travers Cornwell Boy, Second Class (No J/42563).

I got the letters from my old headmaster at Walton Road School and from my boss at Whitbread's, and took them to the recruiting officer, who said they would do fine. I signed the forms and was given a rail ticket to Plymouth. I am to start my training at HMS *Vivid*, Keyham Naval Barracks in Devonport. The recruiting officer told me that the training normally takes two years, but they have speeded things up so that it will take only six months. They have an urgent need for us boys to go to sea and join the fighting ships. I'm to be paid sixpence a week, when my training's over I'll be paid a shilling a week.

I went to the brewery depot and told the manager that I was going off to war. He shook my hand and told me there'd be a job for me at the brewery when the war was over.

Then I went to where Jeb was at the dray cart and told him the news. He looked at me for a bit, then held out his hand for me to shake. I took it and he shook my hand firmly and gave me a smile.

"You're a brave boy, Jack," he said. "And good company. I'll miss having you to talk with when I'm doing my rounds. Make sure you come back safe so you can join me on the cart again."

"I will," I assured him.

Then I shook his hand again and set off home to pack my bags. After that, I sat down and wrote a letter to Dad.

Dear Dad,

Good news! I have joined the navy, so I will be fighting the Hun very soon! I start my training tomorrow at HMS Vivid. I will think of you when I am sailing the waves, sinking the German battleships and their U-boats. I will do my duty, just as you always say, and hope I make you proud of me.

I remain your ever-loving son,

Jack

PART 2

TRAINING
HMS VIVID, DEVONPORT
LONDON 1915 – 1916

29th July 1915

Today I said goodbye to Ma, George, Fred, little Lily and Alice.

I got to Paddington station to catch my train. The station was packed, mainly with men and boys also going down to Plymouth. Many of them were in uniform – junior officers, able-bodied seamen and cadets – but quite a few were in their civvies, like I was. Most of those wearing ordinary clothes were boys of about my age, maybe a little older.

I found myself a seat inside a carriage with three other boys, all Londoners. It was obvious we were all going to the same place for the same reason so we shook hands and introduced ourselves.

"I'm Jack Cornwell," I said. "From East Ham."

"Jimmy Mac," said the tallest, a red-haired boy, as he shook my hand. He gestured his thumb at the smaller boy sitting next to him. "This is my cousin, Bobby. We're from Camden Town."

"I live just round the corner from him," said Bobby. "We grew up together."

"T-Terry," said the fourth one. "I-I'm...". We nodded

politely and waited for him to find his words. "I'm from Pa-Paddington."

"You didn't have far to come then." Jimmy grinned.

I was pleased that Jimmy and Bobby didn't make fun of Terry because of his stammer. When I was at school we had a kid who stammered, and some of the other kids used to be really cruel to him. My dad says that picking on someone weaker than yourself is the coward's way. He says it's the duty of the strong to protect the weak. I suppose that's why we went to war with Germany, to protect the smaller and weaker countries they attacked.

The train journey to Plymouth was really long. It took hours and hours. Luckily my ma had packed me some sandwiches for the journey, and so had Terry's. Jimmy and Bobby had just a piece of bread and dripping each, which wasn't much, so me and Terry shared our food with them. Jimmy promised to pay us back when we got our first pay.

"You d-don't have to p-pay me back," said Terry. "That's what pa-pals are for."

Jimmy smiled. "Yes!" he said. "That's us! The Four Pals!"

I feel really good about having made these friends so quickly. I'm sure it will help me settle in so far away from home.

30th July 1915

Yesterday we all arrived at HMS *Vivid* Keyham Barracks, in Devonport, Plymouth.

We were immediately given our uniforms and equipment and put into groups of twenty. Each group is called a mess. I was pleased that I am in the same mess as Jimmy, Bobby and Terry, so we can still be the Four Pals together!

I thought HMS *Vivid* was going to be a ship, but it turns out to be part of the barracks, which are on land, although it is next to the docks.

The name "barracks" strikes me as wrong, because it sounds like a place with lots of long huts. But Keyham Barracks is more like a small town. It even has its own church on the site, which shows how big it is. It looks as if there are thousands of people here, either training or working. I think it is going to take me a while to get used to this place and find out where everything is, and especially what I have to do in my training.

14th August 1915

I've been here two weeks now and I'm getting the hang of things. The difficult thing at first was getting used to sleeping in a hammock instead of a bed. A hammock is like a sheet that hangs between two hooks. You have to hang it up yourself at night before going to bed, then take it down in the morning.

I don't know why we have to sleep in hammocks instead of proper beds. Jimmy says it's because there's not a lot of room below decks on ships, and beds would take up too much space. But I've noticed that sometimes Jimmy says things as if they are true, even when he doesn't really know about them. This doesn't mean he tells lies. It just means if he doesn't know why something happens, he comes up with a reason of his own, and sometimes he's right, sometimes he's wrong.

Someone else in our mess said the reason sailors sleep in hammocks is because when ships are at sea they move about all over the place, because of the winds and high seas, and a hammock is easier than a bed because it swings with the ship when it moves. That doesn't make sense to me because it could swing too hard and throw you out of bed. I'm sure I'll find out the real reason why we sleep in hammocks later.

The day's routine at the Barracks goes like this:

At half-past five in the morning the bugle is sounded to wake us up and call us to attention – I'm told the morning bugle doesn't sound until a quarter to six in winter – (a whole quarter of an hour more to sleep!) We roll up our hammocks, then we have prayers. After prayers we clean and tidy up our quarters until eight o'clock. Then we eat breakfast.

At half past eight we are inspected by the officer of the day, who checks that our boots are polished and our uniforms are clean and we have washed, including under our fingernails. I am used to this because we used to have this sort of inspection when I was in the Boy Scouts in Manor Park.

By nine o'clock we start our classes. The classes vary, depending on what we are due to learn that day. During our first week we learnt all about our kit. We learned how to roll our hammocks, how to sling them up and take them down. We also learned about the importance of washing and looking after our clothes, including sewing and mending.

This last week we have been learning semaphore, which is sending messages using flags. Luckily for me, I already did semaphore in the Boy Scouts. Next week we will have a week learning bends and hitches, which means learning to tie different sorts of knots. Once more, I shall be fine here because I did knots in the Scouts as well.

At noon we stop for dinner; then after that we start work again until three o'clock. Except on Wednesdays and Saturdays, that is. On those two days we get the afternoon off as half-holidays. On the other days we do games, or we practise rowing or sailing.

At five o' clock it's tea time, and after tea we can do what we want until half past eight, providing we don't get into trouble. Often me and the gang find somewhere to kick a football around. Terry is the best footballer of the four of us, though Jimmy likes to think he is.

At half past eight we sling our hammocks and make them ready for the night, then climb in. The bugle goes for "lights out" at nine o'clock, but by then most of us are asleep after the day's hard work. But before I go to sleep I say a prayer for Dad and Arthur, and for God to keep them safe.

16th August 1915

Since I last wrote we had what I'm told is called "an incident". In this case it meant Terry getting badly bullied by another boy in our mess, and we didn't know how to deal with it because we didn't want to make Terry look worse.

The bully was a boy called Ted Meers. He's fifteen years old, like us, but he's big for his age. He comes from somewhere in Kent. Unfortunately, it seems wherever you go, there will always be bullies to make trouble. It was the same when I was at school, and it's the same now I'm in the navy.

What happened was that we came into our mess to put up our hammocks, and Meers shouted at Terry in a nasty way, making fun of his stammer. He started pretending to stammer, saying "D-d-d-do", and his mates started laughing. It upsets me when you see people playing up to bullies like Ted Meers, pretending they like them and laughing at their jokes, when the truth is they're just scared of them. Anyway, Terry went red, and because he was so angry, he couldn't get his words out. He started to say "Shut up", but he could only get out "Sh …" and then he got stuck, and Meers laughed at him and repeated "S-s-sh". I was going to step in, but before I did Jimmy said to Meers, "Leave him alone!"

Meers turned on Jimmy and snapped at him, "You want to make something of it, do you?"

Instantly everyone went silent, because we all knew what Meers was like. He was a bully, but he was also strong, and he was a cheat of a fighter. In our first week he'd got into a fight with a boy from another mess and had kicked him in the leg and when he went down he kicked him in the groin. The boy's screaming brought an officer to see what the trouble was. Meers claimed that he'd only been defending himself after this other boy attacked him and Meers's mates backed him up.

The other boy went to hospital, and I heard he was sent home. Since then, everyone was wary of Meers.

For a moment I thought that Jimmy was going to back down because he'd gone all white in the face, but then he just turned and looked Meers straight in the face and said, "I'm just saying you leave him alone, unless you want to take on both of us."

"Three of us," piped up a voice, and I realized that it was Bobby who'd spoken. So, of course, because we were the Four Pals, I had to speak up as well. "That's four of us," I threw in, and walked over to join Jimmy, Bobby and Terry.

Meers looked at us, and I could see he was thinking hard. Yes, I was pretty sure he could beat any one of us on his own, but he wouldn't have as much chance against four of us. And he was clever enough to know that he couldn't depend on his so-called "mates" if it came to a real fight. People who hang around bullies do it because they want to pretend they're tough, but usually they're not. Get them on their own and they crumble.

Finally Meers sneered. He turned to Terry and said: "So, you're not m-m-man enough. You've got to have your mates to look after you. Baby!"

With that Meers turned and went out of the hut, heading for the toilet block. There was an awkward silence in the hut, and then his cronies went after him. Terry looked furious.

"You s-shouldn't have s-said anything!" He forced the words out angrily to Jimmy.

Jimmy stared at him, stunned. "Well thanks for nothing, pal!" he snapped back. "I just put my head on the line for you!"

"I d-didn't need it!" said Terry. Then he went to his hammock and started putting it up. His ears were all red and I could see how angry he was.

Jimmy was also angry. He glared at Terry, and then stormed outside the hut.

Bobby and I exchanged sympathetic looks. We both

knew what was going on. In Terry's case, he didn't want to look as if he had to have someone to take care of him. He wanted to be seen to stand up for himself, even though we all knew that if it came to a fight, Meers would slaughter Terry.

From Jimmy's point of view, he'd put himself at risk to save Terry from getting beaten up by Meers. When Jimmy spoke up, he wasn't to know that me and Bobby would add our voices as well.

"What are we going to do?" asked Bobby quietly, looking towards Terry. At the open door of our hut we could see Jimmy standing outside.

I shook my head. "I don't know," I admitted. "We've got to talk to them. We can't have the Four Pals splitting up like this."

"You're right." Bobby nodded. "If you have a word with Terry, I'll have a word with Jimmy."

While Bobby went out to talk to Jimmy, I walked over to where Terry was putting the finishing touches to his hammock. He didn't turn round to look at me, even though he must have heard the sound of my boots walking towards him on the wooden floor. And I could have been Meers coming after him.

"Terry," I said.

"I d-don't want to t-talk about it," he said. His voice was all gruff and choked, and I suddenly realized that he was crying. Though I didn't know if he was for sure, because he wouldn't turn and face me.

"You can't let someone like Meers break up the Four Pals," I said. "We've been good for each other. If we break up like this, then Meers has won, whatever happens." I waited for Terry to reply, and when he didn't I carried on. "All right, Jimmy shouldn't have spoken up like that. But he did it because he's your mate. Like I am. Like Bobby is. We're pals, and pals look after one another."

Terry still didn't speak, but he'd stopped messing with his hammock. He stood there, listening, so I carried on talking.

"Admit it, Jimmy could have got himself badly beaten up standing up to Meers the way he did. Remember what happened to that boy in that other mess, the one Meers kicked who got sent home. Trust me, Terry, Jimmy didn't do what he did to upset you. You know what Jimmy's like, his mouth opens before his brain starts thinking."

At this, Terry nodded. "T-true," he said quietly. And he gave a sniff and he wiped his face with his sleeve.

"So, I think you ought to shake hands with him, so we can be the Four Pals again," I said.

I heard heavy clumping footsteps on the floorboards behind me, and I whirled round, thinking it might be Meers and some of his mates, but it was Jimmy and Bobby.

"I was just thinking the same," said Jimmy. He stuck out his hand towards Terry. "I'm sorry, Terry. I spoke out of turn, and I was wrong. Are we still mates?"

Terry hesitated, then he wiped his face with his sleeve again and turned to face us. His face was all tightly stretched across his cheekbones, and I could see from his eyes that he had been crying. He looked at Jimmy's outstretched hand then he took it and shook it.

"M-mates," he said, nodding firmly. Then he gulped and added, "I'm s-sorry, J...".

Jimmy shook his head. "No need to say sorry, Terry," he said. "Let's just not say any more about it." Then he grinned. "And the four of us should stick together. That way, Meers won't try it on any of us, cos he'll always be taking on four. And even for him, that's two too many."

"Good!" agreed Bobby. "Now I suggest we finish our hammocks and get some sleep. We've got a hard day in the morning."

I felt relieved as I fixed up my hammock to think that the Four Pals hadn't broken up. But I knew that the problem of Meers wouldn't go away. And some day, I was sure, Terry would find himself standing up to Meers on his own, and getting hurt.

20th August 1915

Today I got a letter from Dad. I was so pleased.

Dear Jack,

Thanks for your letter. So you are going to be a sailor! I'm really proud of you. You will cut a fine figure in your uniform. Always remember that whatever happens, do your duty. Avoid bad company. I know you will because you are a good and honest boy, and have been brought up to always do the Right Thing.

Things here are much the same as they have been. I would like to be in the action more, but I will be ready if and when the Hun attack us.

The men I am with are good blokes. All of us know that we are fighting for our families. Just the same as you will be doing soon.

I'm thinking of you.

Your loving,

Dad

It's been ages since I've heard from him, and I've been wondering how he was. For that reason, it's been lucky for me that we're kept so busy, and I'm so tired when we finish for the day that I go to sleep straight away. Dad didn't say anything about his health, so I hope he's all right and his bronchitis is being kept at bay.

30th August 1915

Today our mess went out on the sea! We took a boat out under the command of a lieutenant, rowing with oars, ten to each side. It was to give us the experience of dealing with the swell of the sea, and controlling a boat according to whether it's an ebb tide (going out) or a flow (coming in).

The sea was quite rough and a few of the boys got sick. I was lucky, I didn't. I seemed to be able to handle the way the boat went up and down. Bobby was sick, so was Meers and two of the other boys. But the lieutenant wouldn't let them stop rowing. When the boat came back to shore, the four who were sick then had to clean the boat.

6th September 1915

Today I had a letter from Ma. It was short, but it meant a lot to me because I know how hard it is for her to put her thoughts down on paper. She says that George and Fred are behaving themselves. Everything is all right at home. Bill Moore, one of our neighbours who was fighting in France, has been killed, and they are worried that Evie Moore, his wife, might do something silly to herself because they were a very close couple. Ma says she and Alice are going to keep an eye on Evie Moore and make sure she is all right. Ma also says that she is thinking of having chickens in the back yard as a way of making sure they get eggs at home.

My guess is Alice gave Ma some help writing the letter. Alice writes and spells really well. She could have got herself a good career, if she had been born somewhere other than East Ham. It seems all the women from where we live have to go into factories, or else do cleaning work. To get on in this world you need education, and education costs money. Everyone says it's a waste of time to educate girls because they're going to get married and have children. I know that's what Dad says, but I think that's a pity in Alice's case.

10th September 1915

I've been given a great honour. The commander of the cadet school at HMS *Vivid* has appointed me to the post of his messenger. This means that at certain times of day I report to his office and collect and deliver messages from him to other high-ranking people at the base. The officer in charge of our mess says this shows that I'm considered to be especially honest, trustworthy and reliable. I've written to Dad to tell him about this. I know he'll be very proud. I've tried to play it down in my letter because I don't want him to think I'm boasting. But I want him to know that I'm doing my duty well enough for the commander to believe I can do this important job.

The lessons we are doing in the mornings are getting much harder. Signalling by semaphore and the different sorts of knots were things I'd already done in the Scouts, so that was easy for me. Since then it's all been new. We've learned about the compass and how to steer by it. Also how to rig and sail a small boat. There have been lessons in throwing the lead to take soundings, as well as how to cast and weigh the anchor.

Yesterday we had a lesson on lights, which are very important when you are in a ship at sea at night. This was about what different lights mean when you see a ship in the distance.

20th September 1915

Last night we had a concert in the gallery in the drill shed, which becomes a sort of theatre. The drill shed isn't a place where there's drill, which is what you'd think from its name, but is part of the canteen.

The concert was good. Some of the sailors took turns to do sketches and sing songs, and we all joined in with the singing. It seemed strange to be sitting in a concert when there was a war going on, but our officer says that there has to be room for some fun, otherwise this life would be just hard work and misery. Personally, I don't think there's anything wrong with hard work – it's how we get on. And where would we be in this war if we didn't work hard to train and learn how to fight and defeat the enemy?

I enjoyed the concert, though. The comedy sketches were funny enough, with some of the men pretending to fall off the stage, and toppling over, and throwing flour at one another. And the songs were good too, especially the rousing songs about winning the war. They made me want to get out there and do my bit even more!

24th September 1915

Trouble with Meers again this afternoon. Me, Jimmy and Bobby were out on the playing field, kicking a ball about with some of the other boys. Terry wasn't with us because he'd gone to see one of the chief petty officers about some pictures of knots he'd had to do. Terry turns out to be quite a good artist and this CPO had asked him if he'd draw some pictures of different sorts of knots so he could use them with other cadets. The next thing we knew, a boy from another mess was running towards us shouting "Fight! Fight!"

Instantly we stopped playing football and went running after him, and found Terry and Meers going hard at it behind one of the long huts. Both of them had blood on their mouths and blood coming from their noses, and Terry had a big nasty bruise over one eye.

Bobby made a move to run in and jump on Meers, but I grabbed him and stopped him. So long as Meers didn't do anything nasty and cheating, like kicking Terry like he'd kicked that other boy, it was a fair fight. Well, it was almost a fair fight. After all, Meers was much bigger than Terry.

As we watched, Meers swung a hard punch at Terry, but Terry managed to duck down and Meers's fist sailed over Terry's head. Then, so quickly that I hardly saw it, Terry jerked back up and brought his fist up hard under Meers's chin. We all heard the crack, though whether it was the sound of Meers's chin bone cracking, or Terry's fingers, I couldn't tell. Certainly, if it had been Terry's fingers, it wasn't stopping him because Terry stepped back, and then swung a punch with his other fist, straight into Meers's face.

Meers couldn't defend himself. That crack on his chin had made him groggy and his hands had dropped down by his side, so Terry's fist just thudded into his mouth, and Meers toppled backwards.

Meers lay there on the ground. We could tell he was conscious, but only just. His eyelids were flickering, like he was trying to keep them open but they wanted to stay shut. Terry stood, his fists ready, panting and waiting for Meers to get up. Then a voice boomed out behind us, demanding, "What's going on here?"

We all turned, then sprang to attention. A CPO was standing there, glaring at us. Even Terry moved to stand to attention, though I noticed he winced as he did so.

The CPO looked at us, and then at Meers lying on the ground, then at Terry, then back at us again and demanded sternly, "I asked: what's going on here?"

"Boxing, sir!" Jimmy replied quickly.

Bobby and I looked at him, stunned, then swung our eyes back to the CPO.

"Boxing?" echoed the CPO.

"Yes, sir," answered Jimmy.

I suppose it wasn't actually a lie. But it wasn't the truth, either.

The CPO stood looking at us for a moment. Then he pointed at Meers, and then at four of the boys nearest to Meers and said, "You, you, you and you. Take him to sick bay." Turning to Terry he said, "And you go to sick bay too. Get yourself seen to. Then you'll report to my office. Is that understood?"

"Y-y-yes, sir," said Terry.

Later, me, Jimmy and Bobby were hanging around close to the CPO's office while Terry and Meers were inside. We were eager to find out what the CPO said to them both. They were in there for ages. Finally the door opened and they came out. Meers said something to Terry, Terry just looked at him, and then Meers walked off. He passed us, but he didn't say anything, just gave us a glare and then trudged on.

"What happened?" asked Jimmy, gesturing at the CPO's office.

63

"He s-said if we d-did it again we'd be in b-big trouble," said Terry. "Then he t-told us to sh-shake hands," said Terry. "So we did."

"But what was all that just now?" asked Bobby. "What did Meers say to you?"

"He s-said I was tougher than he th-thought, and he wanted to b-be my p-pal." Terry grinned. "I told him I've already g-got three pals."

We all laughed, and Jimmy slapped Terry on the back.

"Good one!" he said. "I don't think you'll have any more trouble from Meers!"

1st October 1915

Today I spent time writing letters to Ma and all at home, to Dad in Colchester, and to Arthur in France. I didn't want to tell them how hard the work is here in case they think I'm complaining. And they're all having things a lot harder than I am. So I wrote and told them about the food and how good it is, because it is. We get a good breakfast. Usually it's sausages and sometimes – if there are any – we get an egg with it. We usually have fish for breakfast as well, a kipper or a bloater. We also get corned beef, which is very filling, and a good wedge of cheese, and in the evening we get a basin of hot cocoa, which is really good.

After I had written the letters I worried that Arthur might get upset because I guess his rations at the front won't be anything like that, and I don't want to make him feel jealous and think my life is getting soft. Life here is far from soft.

It's not so much the hard physical work that wears me out as the brain work, with all the things we have to remember. A lot of them are to do with arithmetic and angles. Like boxing the compass, for instance. This is when we have to remember all 32 points of the compass clockwise from north. Each point is at eleven and a quarter degrees, and you have to be able to work out the whole way round the compass at these intervals. They say things will get easier once every ship in the navy is using the gryocompass, which is marked in degrees around a circle from 0 to 360, but at the moment we have to work everything out in points.

18th October 1915

Bobby got a letter today from his Ma which told him his two older brothers, Ted and Stan, were both dead, killed in action. Bobby did his best not to cry in front of us, but I could see his lips were trembling and his eyes were red. I didn't know what was in the letter at the time, but I could see he was upset by it, so I asked him if he was all right. He nodded and went out, taking the letter with him.

A short while later he came back into the mess and handed me the letter to read, then went out again. I read it, then told Jimmy and Terry what was in it. Jimmy was so shocked that he nearly fell over, and I kicked myself for not remembering that he and Bobby were cousins, so Ted and Stan had been Jimmy's cousins as well. Jimmy turned and went out, looking very upset.

Terry and I didn't know quite what to do. In the end, we went outside and found Bobby and Jimmy sitting on a tree stump.

"I'm sorry, Jimmy," I said. "I forgot they were your cousins. I didn't mean to blurt it out like that."

Jimmy shook his head. "That's all right, Jack," he said.

"Anyway, me and Bobby are going to have some quiet time on our own for a bit."

"Of course," I said.

Me and Terry left them there. There's not a lot to say when something like that happens.

19th October 1915

Today Jimmy was a lot better. Bobby still looked pale and unhappy, but that's understandable. I'd be the same if I got that same news about Dad and Arthur. I wonder where Bobby's brothers were killed? I wonder if it is anywhere near where Arthur's fighting? I especially worry about Dad, even though he's in England. He's not as young as most of the men in the army. I know he says he's an old soldier, and he's as tough as old boots, but he needs to take care of himself.

8th November 1915

We have been doing lessons in gunnery. These are the lessons I have been looking forward to the most because I want to be a gunner on a ship, and fire shells at the Germans and sink their ships. The truth is, though, I've found these lessons to be the hardest of all. It's not just about how to fire a gun, that would be easy. It's about angles of projectiles, and velocity, and all sorts of arithmetic stuff. A naval gun is not just like a rifle or a pistol, it's a big and very complicated piece of machinery with lots of parts that can go wrong. It also needs a very big crew to man, load and fire it. The whole business of loading it and firing it is pretty complicated. But I am determined to learn all there is to know.

25th December 1916

Christmas Day. Today we had a proper Christmas dinner – turkey, roast potatoes, vegetables and gravy, with a great Christmas pudding to follow. It was the best meal I've ever had. After it we all drank a toast to the King.

It seemed strange to be having Christmas away from home, but in a way it felt like home because of being part of the Four Pals. They've become like family. It sounds strange to say, but they seem more like brothers to me than George and Fred. That said, I thought of George and Fred and Lily and Alice at home with Ma, and said a prayer for them. When all this is over, we shall have our own Christmas together.

8th January 1916.

My birthday. I am sixteen years old and in the navy. Well, at the moment I am still in training but in just a few weeks' time I shall be qualified as a Boy, First Class, and then I will be assigned a ship. It would be great if all four of us – me, Jimmy, Bobby and Terry – were assigned to the same ship, so the Four Pals would stick together. In the army they have regiments known as the Pals, where friends who've got together form a regiment of their own and go off to fight in the war together. But in those cases the Pals are usually all from the same village, or the same local area, and there are enough to form a whole regiment. With us there are just four of us. Also, it's not just numbers in ships, they need men and boys with different skills. In the army it's really just about being able to use a rifle.

28th January 1916

The Government have introduced conscription. This means that every man over the age of eighteen has to go into the services and fight. I think this is only right. Britain is at war and needs every man she can get if we are not to lose to the Germans.

This war has been going on for a long while. I don't see that it can keep on going like this. Men are dying all the time and whole countries are being destroyed. I sometimes think that everyone's forgotten what this war is all about. All I know is that we have to beat the Germans, otherwise they will rule us.

Today the gunnery officer asked me to stay behind after the lesson. I was worried that he was going to make me stay behind and do some of the calculations again. I was surprised when he said that he was impressed with my work in the gunnery lessons, and asked me if I had thought about studying to be a sight setter or gun layer.

What a sight setter does is this: on the big gun there is a brass disc. The sight setter turns this brass disc to make the muzzle of the big gun go up, or go down, to make sure the shells that the gun fires hit on the target. If the sight setter gets it wrong, it means the shells will miss the target.

Being a sight setter is a really important job. It's not always done by boys, many men do it as well. The gunnery officer told me he has been keeping an eye on the way I apply myself to my lessons, and he thinks I could be a sight setter if I wanted to.

The trouble is, to qualify as a sight setter means extra training. As it stands, me and the rest of our mess will pass out as Boys, First Class, next month. If I volunteer to stay on and train as a sight setter, this means another two months' training.

I thanked the gunnery officer and said I would like to train. But afterwards I wondered if I'd done the right thing. If I leave the training camp next month when I pass out as a Boy, First Class, then I'll go straight on to a ship and be taking my part in the war. If I stay on for extra training to be a sight setter, it could be another eight or nine weeks before I get on board a ship.

I didn't know what to do, so I talked about it afterwards with the other three. Bobby was impressed when I told him and said he wished he'd been asked, but Jimmy and Terry felt differently.

"I want to get to grips with the Germans as soon as I can," stated Jimmy.

"M-me t-too," nodded Terry.

Bobby shook his head. "Being a sight setter means being part of a gun crew," he said. "Actually being on deck, firing shells at the Hun. Fighting them face-to-face. As ordinary sailors, we could end up being below deck and never seeing the enemy at all."

This time it was Jimmy's turn to shake his head. "That may be so," he said, "but I don't want to wait. I want to get out there! If I had my way, I'd be on a warship already, instead of being stuck in lessons day after day."

"We have to learn," put in Terry.

"I've learned all I need to know," said Jimmy. "Come February, I shall be on a ship!"

Bobby looked at me. "Well, Jack?" he asked. "What are you going to do?"

"I've already told the gunnery officer I will," I said.

"You can tell him you've changed your mind," said Jimmy. "Tell him you want to get out there and fight the Hun as soon as you can!"

I thought it over, looking at their expectant faces as I did so. All of them were waiting, wondering what I was going to do. I sighed and shook my head.

"I've got to do it," I said. "Before I started, I wanted to be a gunner on a ship. I'm being given a chance."

They fell silent, and Jimmy looked particularly unhappy. "It'll be the end of the Four Pals," he said sadly.

"No it won't," I said. "We'll always be pals. And after

the war we can get together and be the Four Pals again." I grinned. "Until then you lot will just have to be the Three Musketeers."

19th February 1916

Today our mess completed our basic training and have all passed out. I am now Boy, First Class!

Me and the gang shook hands to congratulate one another, then they went off to pack up their things. They are all to be assigned to their ships, and they will be shipping out early tomorrow, while I start my training to be a sight setter. I wonder if the four of us really will meet up again? I hope so.

20th February 1916

It takes a great deal more than most people think to make a gun work.

When a shell arrives, it's put into a loading tray next to

the breech, which is the end of the gun's firing tube – the long gun barrel. When the breech is opened, the loading tray moves in front of the breech and a man with a ramrod – which is like a hard cloth pad on the end of a long pole – pushes the shell into the breech. This ramrod is the same sort of thing they once used to push cannonballs and gunpowder into the old-fashioned cannons of Drake and Nelson!

Another man puts the cordite – the explosive that fires the shell – into the breech and the ramrodder pushes the cordite in after the shell, followed by a firing pin. The breech door is then shut. This automatically pushes the loading tray for the shells ready for the loader to put the next shell on.

The gunner pulls a trigger – a cord that hangs out of the back of the breech – which sets off the firing pin and explodes the cordite. The explosion is so powerful, it can fire a shell for miles.

If that sounds complicated, it gets worse because the gun has to move left and right, as well as up and down, to make sure that the shell hits the target when it's fired.

To move the gun there are two men, both sitting on seats fixed to the gun. One man is in charge of elevation, which is raising or lowering the gun barrel. The other man is in charge of traverse, which means moving the barrel from side to side, to the left and right.

None of the gun crew can actually see the target they're aiming at. They act on instructions they receive from the gunnery officer. And the person who relays the instructions from the gunnery officer to the men who move the gun up or down is me, the sight setter or gun layer.

On a ship the gunnery officer is in a conning tower, which is high up in the centre of the ship. He can see the enemy and he works out what angle the gun needs to be at to hit the target. He calls his instructions to the sight setter through a telephone line, and the setter receives them through headphones.

Because we were only training, we used the gun that's set up in the grounds of the barracks. Also, because we were training and they didn't want to waste valuable ammunition, we just did it with dummy shells without cordite and firing pins.

The gunnery officer called out different angles to me through the headphones. To begin with, he wanted me to set the gun so that it would hit a target 6,000 yards away, so he called out "6,000!". I turned the brass disc on the gun until the notch that was marked 6,000 was in line with the arrow on the brass plate beneath it. Then the gunnery officer called out, "Down 300!". I turned the disc so that the arrow went down 300 to 5,700. Then the gunnery officer called out "Up 500!", and I turned the disc the other way, so that the arrow went up past 6,000 to 6,200. That meant the gun was now aimed at a target 6,200 yards away.

The gun crew is made up of ten – crew leader, shell loader, elevation, traverse, ramrodder, fuses, cordite, package disposer, reserve, and me – sight setter. If it sounds like a lot of men just to fire one gun, there are even more involved! There are the men who carry the shells up to the gun. There are the men who put the fuses in the shells and arm them ready to be fired. (Shells can't be armed before they are ready to be fired because it would be too dangerous to have them lying around armed and all set to explode.) There are also the men in the cordite room, responsible for sending up the plugs of cordite to fire the gun.

The reason so many men are needed is so that the gun can fire and be reloaded quickly. When a gun crew is working fast together, a gun can fire ten shells a minute.

17th March 1916

The war continues. I've had no news of Dad or Arthur for a while yet. I hope they are keeping well, but the news from the front is confused. Some reports say we are winning and the Germans have been pushed back, yet on the same day there'll be reports that the Germans have made ground.

The only thing that everyone seems to agree on are the casualty figures. I pray every night that Arthur is safe, and that we will win this war.

26th April 1916

I am now fully qualified as a gun layer or sight setter.

I was given my papers, and my travel orders and travel dockets for the journey to the ship I've been assigned to. It is the cruiser HMS *Chester*, which is based in Rosyth in Scotland. Today is one of the proudest days of my life!

I don't have to report to HMS *Chester* until next Monday, the 2nd of May, so I've been given leave to go home and spend a few days with Ma and the family. It will be good to see them and catch up with their news, and the news from Dad and Arthur. It's been almost nine months since I was home.

PART 3

BACK HOME AND ONWARD!

29th April 1916

It was so good to see Ma and the family again. George, Fred and little Lily have all grown up so much since last July.

George and Fred were really jealous of my uniform and wanted to try it on, but I said no. This uniform had to be earned. I let them wear my cap, though. Alice arrived with a young man she's been walking out with. His name is Charles and he's in a reserved occupation, which is why he isn't fighting in the war.

Just this morning Ma had letters from Dad in Colchester, and Arthur from France. My guess is that Dad's written to me in Devonport, and his letter will be forwarded on to me. At least, I hope it will be.

There have been many deaths of men in our neighbourhood, men who had been fighting overseas. Most of them had died in France and Belgium, but one of our neighbours, Mrs Clare, lost her son John in Gallipoli, which is in Turkey. According to George, who has been following the war while I've been away, Gallipoli was a terrible defeat for our side. We lost half our army in casualties, about a quarter of a million men. I told George off for spreading stories about defeats. I explained we should only be talking about our victories because spreading stories about our defeats lowers morale among our soldiers and sailors.

"So have I lowered your morale then, Jack?" asked George.

I could tell by the smile on his face that he was just being cheeky, but I thought it was time to be serious with him. "No, you haven't, George," I replied. "Because I know we're going to win this war. But there are plenty of enemies who are doing their best to stop us, and that sort of talk only helps them. You don't want to be the one who helps our enemies attack Dad and Arthur, do you?" The mention of Dad, and the reminder that Arthur was out in France fighting, made George look uncomfortable.

"I was only joking you, Jack," he said defensively.

"Well it's not something we should joke about," I told him. "This war is a serious business."

"Can we stop talking about the war for a bit?" pleaded Ma. "Jack's home after being away for nine months. We ought to be enjoying him being here, instead of going on about the war. He'll be off to it soon enough."

"Quite right," said Alice. "Let's put the kettle on for a cup of tea, and I'll make us some sandwiches."

So that's what we did. We settled down to chatter about all manner of things, and for a short while it almost seemed as if the war wasn't happening. But you only had to

look at the photos of Dad and Arthur on the mantelpiece
to be reminded it was.

1st May 1916

My last night at home in East Ham. Tomorrow morning
I will go to King's Cross station and catch the train to
Rosyth in Scotland. It's a really long train journey which
is going to take most of the day. The train goes right up
England and into Scotland to just past Edinburgh, which
is on the Firth of Forth, where HMS *Chester* is moored.
I've never been north of London, so this journey will be a
real adventure. But not as much of an adventure as actually
going to sea and taking part in the war and doing my bit,
fighting the Germans.

It's been strange, these last few days. Even though it's
been good to see Ma, George, Fred, Lily and Alice, I know
I'm not the same Jack Cornwell I was just nine months
ago, when I left to go to HMS *Vivid* and start my training.
Being away from home all that time and training, and
everything else, has made me into someone else. I know
people say I'm not a man yet, but I know I'm not a boy any
more. My adventures at HMS *Vivid*, all the things I've done

and the people I've mixed with, have put me apart from George and Ernest. Even from Ma. I feel I know what the war is about now. It's about battle – man against man, ship against ship, gun against gun. It's about facing every day as if it will be your last, and not letting it make you afraid.

2nd May 1916

I got off the train in Rosyth and set off to find HMS *Chester*, my kitbag over my shoulder. I'd been told that it was at anchor, so I'd have to walk along the dock until I came to the small boats that ferried sailors out to their ships. The train journey had been a long one, and it was getting dark. I was getting near to the place on the quay where the small boats left when I heard a voice call out: "Hello, shipmate!" I looked behind me, but I couldn't see anyone. Then I looked to where a stack of oil drums were piled up, and I noticed a boot sticking out from behind them. I went towards the stack of oil drums, but being very careful. I'd heard that thieves sometimes hung around the docks, waiting to attack sailors and roll them for their money. I kept well clear of the oil drums as I went round to the other side. A sailor was lying on the ground, and at first I thought he must be injured, but then he smiled and waved.

"Hello, shipmate!" he said again. "I heard you coming!"

I moved nearer to him, and as I did so the smell of drink came off him, and I realized that he was so drunk he couldn't stand up.

"You're drunk," I said.

"I am," he admitted. "Drunk as a judge."

He tried to push himself up off the ground, but instead he fell back. I put down my kitbag and moved towards him to try and help him up, but keeping myself clear of his mouth in case he was suddenly sick and vomited over my uniform. I got my hands under his arms and managed to help him struggle to his feet. Once he was up, he reached out and held on to the nearest oil drum to help him balance. It was lucky the drums were full. If they'd been empty he'd have pulled them over on top of him.

"Where are you bound, shipmate?" he asked.

"HMS *Chester*," I replied.

He smiled broadly again. "That's my ship!" he said. "Will you give a shipmate a hand and help him get on board?"

I gave him a doubtful look. "I don't know if that's a good idea, in your condition," I said. "You'll be caught for being drunk and disorderly."

"Better than being court-martialled for desertion," he said.

"Desertion?" I said, shocked.

"Or maybe just absent without leave," he added. He blinked a few times, and then held out one hand. "My name's Wally," he said. "Wally Bones."

"Jack Cornwell," I shook his hand.

"The thing is, Jack, I was with some pals ashore on leave and I sort of got separated from them," Wally explained. "I found a girl and thought I'd have some fun. So they went off back to the ship. Me and the girl had our fun and a lot of drink, and then the next thing I knew I was out on the street, trying to get back to the good old *Chester*. But I only got this far before my legs packed up."

"For someone's who's as drunk as you are, you don't sound drunk," I said.

"That's true," agreed Wally. "That's the way it is with me. My mouth will always work when I'm drunk. It's my body, especially my legs, that doesn't. Mind, tomorrow I will have a headache."

I looked at Wally and thought about escorting him back to the ship. I was worried about arriving for my first ever duty helping to carry a man who was drunk in uniform. I'd never been drunk in my life. I'd never touched strong drink – a glass of ginger beer was enough for me. Would they think I was the same as him, his drinking companion? But I couldn't let him lie here on the ground this way. As Wally said, if he didn't get back to the ship, he'd be charged with being AWOL, or even desertion. And in a time of war that was a treasonable offence.

"All right," I said. "I'll help you. Wait 'til, I've got my kitbag on my shoulder, then lean on me."

Wally smiled an even broader smile. "You're a good pal!" he beamed. "You've just made a friend for life in Wally Bones!"

I heaved my kitbag on to my shoulder, then went to Wally and let him lean against me and put an arm round my shoulder. Then we made our way along the quayside, with him lurching along, his legs going in all directions, and every so often falling down, then hauling himself back up using me as a prop. We reached the dockside where the boats were taking sailors out to their ships. Two sailors eyed us suspiciously as we reached them.

"Where you bound?" one asked.

"The *Chester*," I said.

They looked at Wally, who was just about hanging on to me to stay upright, and the other sailor asked, "What's wrong with him?"

"He's not well," I said. Well, it wasn't a lie.

The two sailors exchanged doubtful looks. "We don't want him being sick in our boat," said one.

"He won't," I assured them, with more confidence than I really felt.

The two sailors helped me get Wally into the boat, and

we set off across the choppy waters of the Firth of Forth. When we reached the *Chester*, three sailors were waiting by the steps.

"Here's Wally!" called one, and the other two let out a cheer and hurried down the steps to help Wally out.

"This here's my pal, Jack Cornwell," said Wally. "He got me here."

One of the sailors patted me on the shoulder. "Good man!" he said, and I realized from his accent he was Welsh. "We was wondering what had happened to Wally. We owe you one!" And with that he carried Wally up the steps. I picked up my kitbag and went up after them. And that's how I arrived for my posting at HMS *Chester*.

9th May 1916

The *Chester* is a very busy ship. It's got a crew of 402, which means there are lots of men on it, crammed into small spaces. You notice it most below deck. There's not much room to hang hammocks, just eighteen inches between each hook, so many hammocks are hung up wherever the men can find a place. At dinner times we cram sixteen to a table, sometimes more, which doesn't give a lot of elbow room when you're eating.

It's also very hot below decks. Ships like this are built for battle, so there are very few portholes. Also the hull is made of metal, which doesn't let in ventilation like the old wooden hulls used to. There are fans which bring in air from the ventilators on deck, but it's so hot that you don't seem to feel the effect of it much.

Wally Bones and his pals have been as good as their word about looking after me. They sought me out the day after I came aboard and helped show me where everything was on the ship. They also spread the word amongst their pals not to play tricks on me. Sometimes when a new boy comes on board the old hands play practical jokes on him for fun. Wally and his friends said if anybody played serious tricks on me (like locking me in a cupboard, or something where I might get seriously hurt) they would take revenge. So it seems it was lucky for me that I found Wally when I did!

12th May 1916

Today we were lined up on deck ready for inspection by Captain Lawson. He's a tall man with a grey beard, very imposing, but – the men say – very fair. He keeps his pet dog on board with him. It's a large sheepdog called Skipper, and when he came to inspect us his dog came with him, following him and stopping when he did. It almost seemed to be sitting to attention at one point. The men say that the dog is really one of the crew, and the man next to me, Dobby, said afterwards that he thinks the dog actually gets a rum ration.

15th May 1916

Today we had gun practice. The men with me on my gun are a good bunch and have worked together before. I'm the only new one in the crew, but they helped me settle in. The man I work with, who sits in the seat controlling the elevation of the gun, is called Patch, and he winked at me as we were preparing. "Don't worry about getting hurt, son," he told me cheerfully. "Just remember, we're sitting on thousands of tons of explosives. If we get hit, we'll all be blown to kingdom come and we won't know a thing about it!"

Our gun has thick armour in front of it, which is fixed to the gun and turns with the gun as it moves, so we're protected. One of the gun crew, the shell loader, Batty, doesn't seem convinced by this, though. "It may look safe enough," he said "but look at that space below the armour. There's a gap between it and the deck. If shrapnel or something comes under there, it'll take our feet off!"

"Then there'll be no more football for you, Batty!" laughed Patch, and the other men laughed too. But Batty didn't laugh.

"I've said all along they ought to put something there as better protection," he insisted.

"Stop complaining," our gun leader, Fred, told him. "It's just as bad for the Germans on their ships."

"That don't make it any better for us!" protested Batty. "I ain't worried about the Germans. I'm worried about getting home alive, and with my feet! I'm supposed to be getting married when this war's over!"

"And she needs your feet to keep her warm, does she?" chuckled Ned. He was on the traverse controls for the gun.

"I think we ought to stop all this talk about getting killed," said Mick, the ramrodder, sternly. "We don't want to upset the boy on his first day with us."

"I'm not upset," I said. "God's on our side. He'll look after us."

"I'd rather have proper armour right down to the deck floor," Batty persisted, still looking sulky. But then he stopped talking about it, as Mick had told him.

17th May 1916

HMS *Chester* is just one of about fifty ships in the Battlecruiser Fleet. The Battle Squadron, which is even bigger and has the really big battleships, is further north, at Scarpa Flow off the Orkney Islands. This is because some of the battleships are so huge, they are too big to be anchored at Rosyth, especially at low tide, so they have to stay in deep water.

The two fleets, our Battlecruiser Fleet and the Battle Squadron, are called the British Grand Fleet when they are together. It's such a great name, the Grand Fleet. And it really is grand.

19th May 1916

There are rumours on board that we will be going into battle soon. There have been reports of some of the German fleet planning to come out into the North Sea and head towards Britain for an attack, supported by a whole fleet of U-boats. Everyone is glad about the news because we have been stuck here for ages with no sign of going into action, and that makes everyone edgy and tense. We are here because we want to fight!

26th May 1916

In spite of the rumours about us going into action, a week has gone by and nothing has happened. We don't know if the reports of the German fleet coming to attack was a true story, or one that someone made up. It's been a month since I left Devonport and I've still seen no action. All I've done is drill and practise and train. Our gun crew can now work together to load and fire the gun like clockwork, but I want us to do it for real, in a battle against the Germans, not just practising and firing unfused shells into the sea as target practice.

29th May 1916

Letters today from both Dad and Ma! Dad wrote:

Dear Jack

Thank you for your letter. I hope you have got your sea legs by now.

I know you can't write and tell me what you're doing, and what ship you're on, so I have to imagine it.

Do they photograph you at all? A pal of mine here says that sometimes the new members of a ship line up with the rest of the crew to have their photos taken. If they do it on your ship, I'd like it if you can let me have a copy.

Sorry this is only a short letter, but things are very busy here, as I am sure you can understand.

I'm sending you some stamps with this so you can write back.

I look forward to seeing you again soon.

Your loving dad

And the one from Ma:

Dear Jack

How are you? We are all well at home. You know Mrs Lester from four doors away, the one we called A.L.? Well she died. The doctor said it was her heart. She was always a good neighbour to us.

Alice says to tell you not to worry about us. Also, to tell you that George and Fred are behaving.

Do write. I like getting your letters.

Love from your

Ma

I shall write back to them both tomorrow. I shall also write letters to Alice, and George.

31st May 1916

This is it! At last! We have been given the order to set sail! And not just the *Chester* and the Battlecruiser Fleet, but the whole British Grand Fleet! We are going into battle! The word is that we are heading for Jutland. I've never heard of Jutland, nor do I know where it is, so I asked Patch.

"Jutland is the northern part of Denmark," he explained. "Although Denmark is neutral, it's right next to

Germany, and they say the German fleet is gathering there, ready to make an attack. So we're going out to meet them and stop them."

This morning the order was given to prepare the *Chester* for action, and at half past eleven we weighed anchor and cast off, in convoy with the other light cruisers and the destroyers in our Battlecruiser Fleet.

As we passed beneath the Forth Bridge, with our crew standing in lines on deck, I had never felt so proud. Looking at all the other ships, with their crews also standing in lines on deck and the fleet stretching in each direction port to starboard and fore and aft, as far as the eye could see, was an incredible sight. There is nothing like a naval fleet leaving harbour and sailing out in the open sea to war. And this is just part of the British Grand Fleet! Once we are out in the North Sea we will be joining up with the Battle Squadron, which is steaming south-east from Scapa Flow. We will meet up and head together towards the coast of Denmark, where reports say the German High Seas Fleet has assembled.

Our fleet is hundreds of ships strong! We are an armada! We are powerful! We are invincible! The British Navy rules the waves!

As we cleared the Firth of Forth, the bugles sounded general quarters, and we all went below to prepare for action.

Shortly after, the bugles sounded again, this time signalling "action stations". We are going into battle! May God be with us.

PART 4

THE BATTLE OF JUTLAND
31st MAY – 2nd JUNE 1916

31st May 1916

It was three o'clock in the afternoon when we met up with the Battle Squadron. We'd been sailing eastwards towards the Danish coast for about three hours since we left the Firth of Forth. The whole of that time our crew had been ready by our gun. I had been standing with my headphones on, waiting for instructions, but so far there had been silence from the gunnery officer. As I stood there I could feel excitement churning inside me. The Germans were out there! Were they heading towards us, or were they hiding, waiting for us in the coves and harbours of Germany?

So far the sea had been calm and the weather good. There was a haze over the sea. It could have been from the effect of sunlight on the water, but it also could have been from the chimneys of the hundreds of ships. Every ship's funnel was pouring out thick smoke, and in this weather it hung lower. The problem was that so many of the ships were burning coal, and coal smoke is much thicker than the smoke from ships like ours, which had oil boilers. This thick smoke can make it difficult for the observers who are watching out for enemy ships, and also for the signallers who have to send messages by flags to the other ships in the fleet.

"The Germans won't come out yet," muttered Ned. "They'll wait 'till our battleships are with us."

"Why?" I asked.

"Because if they attack us now, they could get cut off by our battleships arriving, and they won't want to be trapped by them. The Germans like a clear run between their ships and the coast so they can run for their rivers."

Just then Batty shouted out, "There they are!"

For a moment I thought he meant he'd seen the Germans, but when I looked I saw our Battle Squadron in the distance, heading towards us. Even from this distance, it was a sight to take your breath away. The really big battleships, the dreadnoughts, were enormous. They made some of the other ships look like toys next to them. To give you an idea of how massive these dreadnoughts were, the displacement of our ship, the *Chester*, was 5,185 tons. Dreadnoughts such as Benbow and Iron Duke had a displacement of 25,000 tons – nearly five times as big as our ship. And I thought our ship was big!

Sailing behind and on either side of the dreadnoughts were more cruisers and destroyers. Hundreds of ships, all ready for battle! It was a sight that filled me with pride. The British Grand Fleet on its way to defeat the Hun, and I was part of it! I wished my Dad could see me!

The *Chester* began to turn, and I noticed that the approaching dreadnoughts and the rest of the Battle Squadron were doing the same, and now we were all heading east towards Jutland.

I glanced around at the other men on the gun. Like me, all of them were straining their ears and eyes, staring out towards the horizon, watching for any sign of the German ships. There was a silence on deck. No one hummed a tune, or cracked any jokes, or started telling stories. We were all just watching and waiting. My whole body felt alive, like every nerve ending was alert and waiting, ready to spring into action as soon as the order was given. But all the time there was nothing. Just our own ships, sailing together, yet at a safe distance apart, and the haze of smoke settling over the sea.

We sailed on for about another hour. The whole time I was alert and tense, standing, waiting, ready. I looked towards the other ships, especially the dreadnoughts, with their hulls painted such a dark grey that they almost looked black. The German ships were painted with light grey paint, so each side could recognize its own ships and the enemy from a distance.

More time passed. The swell of the sea rose and fell, the waters getting choppier now, but I remained standing, holding on to the gun mounting, ready for action.

Then suddenly we heard it! The sound of heavy gunfire

just a few miles distant, towards the south-east!

"We've found 'em!" shouted Patch. "Get ready, boys!"

"Signals," said Fred, pointing at one of the nearest ships, and I saw the flags go up with signals to us and the other ships around us, ordering us to change direction. We could all feel the ship begin to turn, heading south-east and gaining speed as it did, pushing towards the German fleet. All the time we could hear the sound of heavy gunfire continuing.

I wondered who the gunfire was coming from. Was it from our own ships or was it from the Germans?

As the ships increased their speed the funnels pushed out more smoke, increasing the haze. I started to pray. Please God, let me be brave!

I knew that all I had to do was follow orders and carry out my duties as I had done hundreds of times during training and practice, but it's a different situation when the enemy are firing live shells at you. I thought of Arthur, who would be going through this hour after hour, day after day, in France. Every day, shells falling on their positions and machine-gun bullets flying at him. Now it was my turn.

All the ships had now turned south-east and we were racing onward, the sea rising, the *Chester* catching the wash from the other ships ahead of us.

I could feel a knot in my stomach as I heard the sounds of battle, of big guns firing, and wondered if the rest of the men felt the same. I knew that, whatever happened, I mustn't let them down. I mustn't let Arthur and Dad down.

I tried to imagine the scene on the rest of the ship. We had trained and practised so many times for action stations and combat, I knew that below deck all of the steel doors were being shut. The medical parties would be getting ready in the sick bays, setting out surgical instruments, medicines and dressings for wounds. The men that would be carrying out emergency fire repairs would be preparing their equipment – mallets, wedges and boxes of sand.

In the turret and the foretop the range-finders would be hard at work, getting ready to pin down the position of the enemy ships and calculate how fast they were travelling and in which direction, then pass that information on to the gunnery officer, who would then pass it on to the gun crews.

Below deck the steel doors would be locked tight with all eight catches instead of the usual two. This would make sure they didn't blow open if there was an explosion.

That was another thing they'd be worrying about below decks – a German shell hitting the store of explosives and fuses. If that happened, it would blow the ship sky-high. That's why the hull of each ship was so heavily armoured.

All this time the thud-thud-thud of the heavy guns in the distance was getting louder, now accompanied by crashes and explosions, the sound of metal being torn apart, and black smoke billowing up in a thick cloud. The battle was raging and the haze of smoke on the water was getting thicker, turning into a fog. We could hardly see those of our ships that were nearest to us, at least not with the naked eye. We all knew we were far enough away from them for a German ship to slip past.

Now, as we got nearer and nearer to the German ships, I had to fight to keep calm. I glanced at the rest of the men in the gun crew. All of them seemed concentrated on manning the gun, getting ready for battle. I wondered if they'd felt the same nervousness as I did when they went into battle for the first time. They'd been joking before, but now all jokiness had gone. I gritted my teeth. I had a job to do. This was no time to start thinking about being afraid.

I continued looking out to sea. My eyes were almost burning now from the strain of peering into the distance, at the ship-filled sea, at the smoke, watching for a ship to appear with a German flag fluttering aloft.

With ships criss-crossing and turning back on their own course, the sea was now getting higher, waves lifting and crashing against the side of the *Chester*. I didn't know what the time was, or how long we had been sailing since the bugles had first blown with the order for "action stations". All I knew was that the enemy was out there, that we were closing in on them, and they were closing in on us, and already the ships at the head of our fleet were engaged in a full-scale battle.

Suddenly I heard the voice of the gunnery officer through my headphones, giving me the elevation for the gun, and I pushed the brass disc to the right marker. Immediately Patch started winding his wheel, bringing the gun down, which meant the Germans were right near us! As Patch stopped winding, Fred pulled the lead connecting to the firing pin. There was an almighty BOOM!! from the gun and it recoiled as the shell hurtled out from the end of the barrel. At the same time the shell casing ejected backwards, where Batty dealt with it, hurling it safely to one side.

Fred opened the breech and the next shell slid into place, and Mick pushed it in with his ramrodder. The gunnery officer's voice through my headphones ordered me to lower the elevation just twenty points, so I changed the setting on the brass disc, and just then I saw the German ships appear from out of the black smoke. There were four of them, light cruisers, the same as us. I heard a thud from one of them – and saw smoke coming from it, then realized they had fired a shell at us. I heard a whining sound and saw the shell getting larger and larger, then instantly the deck near me blew up.

There was a flash of white that almost blinded me, then intense heat as flames leaped up, followed by thick, black smoke, so thick that I couldn't see. I put my hand over my nose and mouth to stop myself from choking on the smoke.

I looked round and saw Ned lying on the deck. He had a massive hole in his chest where a piece of shrapnel had torn into him, almost cutting him in half.

All at once there was another explosion, even louder than the first, right by me, and I heard screaming. The smoke shifted and I could see two men rolling in agony on the deck, and I saw that their legs had been cut off just below the knees.

I stayed standing at my post, waiting for instructions over my headphones to set the gun, and I heard a voice say "six...", then the rest of his words were lost as another explosion hit us. The whole gun seemed to lift up off the deck with the force of the explosion, as if it was being torn off, and I immediately knew I'd been hit. I looked down at my front and saw that parts of my uniform had been torn open, shredded across the chest, and I saw the glint of metal among the tattered blue cloth.

At first my body went numb, but then the pain hit me. I'd never felt pain like it. It felt as if my whole body was on fire, as if my skin had been torn off and I was being burned.

I gritted my teeth against the pain. I wouldn't cry out! The Germans wouldn't beat me! Arthur and his mates were suffering this kind of thing every day, and for months and months. If they could take it, so could I.

I was just turning to look at the rest of my gun crew when there was a BOOOOM!! from an explosion, the force of the blast throwing me back against the metal of the gun. I nearly slipped down, but I managed to grab hold of one of the handles and held on, determined to stay on my feet. I was afraid that if I went down, I'd never get up again, and I had to stay standing. I had to stay by my gun. I was the sight setter. Without me the gun couldn't fire at the enemy.

Even though I couldn't see because of the smoke, I knew that the rest of my crew were either dead, or badly injured like me. But I was certain they'd be sending other men to replace them. And when they did, they'd need me as their sight setter. I would not desert my post.

The pain was really bad now, like red-hot blades cutting into my chest and my shoulders, but it was in my chest where the pain was worse. I looked down at my wounds. The front of my uniform was now soaked in blood and it was sticking to my skin. It sounds stupid but my first thought was: "I'm going to have a devil of a job trying to get this uniform clean!"

I can't die, I told myself. *I have to stay alive and stay here for when the others come to take over the gun. I have to stay at my post. I'm the sight setter. I'm needed here.*

I started to feel sick, and I felt dizzy, though whether that was from the smoke or the bits of metal that had pierced into my chest, I didn't know. Possibly a bit of both. I could feel myself sagging back against the metal of the gun and starting to slide down, but I clenched my teeth and forced myself to stand up. I mustn't sit down. I must keep my eyes open.

All the time I listened, waiting for instructions through my headphones, but I knew the instructions wouldn't come until another gun crew arrived. I waited, but no one appeared.

I could hear other explosions on-board, but further away from my position. The Germans were targeting the rest of our ship.

The pain in my chest was getting more severe now. It was a dull ache, but if I tried to move, or even coughed, a sharp pain shot through me like a burning knife, so I did my best to stay still.

Suddenly I heard footsteps on the deck rushing towards my position. Another gun crew, I thought! We're going after the Germans! I gritted my teeth against the pain in my chest. I hard to hold firm and set the gun sights! But it wasn't a replacement gun crew. It was the ship's medical orderlies, four of them. Three of them began checking on the bodies of the men lying by the gun on the deck, and one of them came over to me.

"Where you hit, son?" he asked.

"Chest," I managed to say.

He knelt down and quickly examined my chest, and reached out a hand to touch it, but I stopped him with my own hand.

"Hurts," I said, my voice shaking.

He nodded. "I bet it does," he said.

He stood up and called to the others. "Boy here badly hurt! Looks like shrapnel in his chest!"

One of the other orderlies came over and joined him, shaking his head. "The others are dead," he announced. "We're heading back to port," he said to me. "We'll get you properly looked at there."

"We can't go back to port!" I protested. "The Germans are here! We have to attack them!"

"We could if we had any guns and gunners to fire them," said the man, "but our guns have been shot to bits. The battle's over for us. We're heading to Immingham."

They gave me an injection of something that knocked me out.

•••

When I came to I was lying on the floor of a cabin inside the ship. I still felt pain in my chest, but not as much as I had before. I suppose the injection they gave me had dulled the pain.

I looked down at my body. My uniform had been torn

open at the front and a bandage had been wrapped around my chest and back. It was heavily bloodstained, I saw the bandage was almost flat, so I knew they must have taken some of the pieces of metal out of me. But it felt as if some of them were still there, stuck in my chest. I coughed, and the pain that went through me was awful, like someone had taken a saw to my lungs.

One of the medical orderlies was attending to another man, but when he heard me cough he got up and came over.

"How are you doing?" he asked.

I opened my mouth to speak, but my mouth was very dry and my throat seemed to have swollen up, and I found I couldn't talk. Instead I gave a slight nod and tried to smile to show him I was all right, even though I knew I wasn't.

"Not long before we get to Immingham," he said. "Then we'll have you sorted out."

"Did...?" I stammered, battling to force the words out, "did ... we ... win?"

The medic's expression clouded.

"The battle's still going on," he said. He must have seen the bitter disappointment on my face, because he forced a smile and said, "Don't worry, I'm sure it's going to be fine. Our fleet's bigger than theirs. I've no doubt we've got the Germans on the run. Old Admiral Jellicoe knows what he's doing!"

I tried to smile with him, but a sudden spasm of pain tore through my chest and I coughed, and I saw blood spurt out of my mouth in a spray. The orderly suddenly looked worried. "Just hold on there, son," he urged. "They'll be able to sort you out at the hospital."

When we arrived at the docks there were ambulances waiting to collect the wounded. I was put on a stretcher and carried to one of the ambulances, and loaded in.

"Won't be long now before we get you to hospital," said a medical orderly cheerfully. "You'll see, once we get you there you'll be as right as rain. We'll soon have you fixed up and back fighting the Hun!"

My head felt like it was swimming and all I could feel was pain. Not just in my chest, but all over my legs, my arms, my head, every part of me felt like it was broken and burning with pain.

I was aware of a face appearing at the door of the ambulance, and I recognized it as being one of the officers, Lieutenant Macfarlane. "See you keep this boy alive!" he told the MO firmly. "He's a hero! Stayed at his post when the rest of his gun crew were killed. If we had an army and a navy of men with the same sort of guts as him, we'd have won this war before now!"

"I was just doing my duty, sir," I said. At least, I hope I said it. My voice had gone all sort of croaky and I wasn't sure if all my words came out properly.

Then the door of the ambulance slammed shut and I could feel the vehicle shudder, then start to move. And, then I passed out.

PART 5

MA

1st June 1916

I'm in hospital. The nurses tell me this is Grimsby General Hospital. One also told me that we won the battle! The matron and the officers have told the hospital staff that they're not supposed to talk about the battle, or mention anything about the war, but this one nurse, Nurse Edwards, who's Welsh, says that I deserve to know.

She says she doesn't know the whole story, but from what she's heard from doctors and men who've come in, and from some of the telephone calls and other things, she says the Germans retreated to their own ports. She doesn't know how many ships the Germans lost, but she says it looks like the German navy has been defeated. Britannia rules the waves! I smiled when she told me this, then the pain in my chest came back again and I started coughing, and there was a lot of blood. Nurse Edwards ran off to get someone, but I passed out before she got back.

Later

I've been given more medicine, which made my head swim. Nurse Edwards was tidying up my bed and she told me the doctors were going to try and operate on me to get the other bits of metal out of my chest. But just as she said this, another nurse, Nurse Mariner, who was passing, told her to shush. Nurse Edwards looked surprised at this, and Nurse Mariner jerked her head and took Nurse Edwards away so I couldn't hear what they were saying. But I could guess it wasn't good news from the way that Nurse Edwards put her hand to her mouth sharply, and then to her eyes, like she was wiping away tears. Then she hurried out of the ward, and Nurse Mariner came over to me and carried on tidying my bed in place of Nurse Edwards.

"What was all that about?" I asked.

Nurse Mariner gave me a smile. "Nothing."

"Whatever it was upset Nurse Edwards," I pointed out.

Nurse Mariner smiled again. "Nurse Edwards gets upset at the slightest thing," she said. "Don't let it worry you."

Then she went on to tidy the next patient's bed.

I lay there for a while, thinking about what had happened. It was true Nurse Edwards did get emotional. I'd only been in the hospital for a short while, and I'd already seen her cry quite a few times. I don't think she was cut out for dealing with men with the sort of injuries suffered in times of war – legs and arms missing, blinded, and lots of them dying right there in the ward.

I was lying there when the matron appeared by my bed. She had a different uniform from the other nurses. They wore white and she wore dark blue. I had heard the nurses talk and they all seemed to be scared of matron. It was like she was their senior officer and they were terrified of doing something wrong and upsetting her. But she didn't look terrifying when she came and stood by my bed. In fact she smiled, and it was a real genuine smile.

"Hello, John," she said.

"Jack," I replied, correcting her. Then I thought how rude that sounded, correcting her like that. And what was worse, correcting someone who was a senior officer, even if it was in a hospital! I forced a smile, and hoped she'd let me off. "John's my given name but everyone calls me Jack," I explained.

Matron smiled again, which surprised me. From the way the nurses talked about her I'd expected her to tell me off for answering her back.

"Jack," she nodded. "That's a good name. Do you have brothers and sisters?"

I said I did, and told her about my brothers Ernest, George and Fred, and my sister, Lily, and also Arthur and Alice. "Arthur's fighting with the infantry in France," I added.

"I'm sure they will be very proud of you," said matron. "I understand you fought bravely in the battle."

"Oh, we carried on all right," I said, remembering what Dad had always told me about not boasting, because no one likes a braggart.

Matron smiled again. "I'm sure you did."

The she went off, and I thought, she's not as scary as the nurses say at all.

Later the doctor, Dr Stephenson, came to see me. "I know you are a brave boy, Jack," he said. "No one could have stayed at his post as you did, as badly wounded as you were, unless they are brave. And, because you are brave and have courage, I know that you will be able to cope with the truth. The fact is, Jack, we can do nothing for you except make you as comfortable as we can. Your injuries are too bad for repair."

I looked at him. He looked so unhappy at having to tell me this.

"So I am going to die?" I asked.

Dr Stephenson nodded. "I'm afraid you are, Jack."

"How long do I have?" I asked.

"I'm guessing you have just a day. Maybe two," he replied. "You are very badly wounded."

I let this sink in. I suppose I had been lucky. I could have been killed along with the rest of the gun crew on the *Chester*. At least I hoped I would have time to say goodbye.

"My Ma –" I began.

"A telegram has been sent to her," said Dr Stephenson. "She's on her way to see you."

"Then I shall stay alive until she gets here," I told him.

Dr Stephenson nodded and patted my hand, and then withdrew to go and attend to other patients.

Later

I don't know how long I have been here in the hospital. The nurses give me medicine to ease the pain of my wounds, and it makes me sleep. There is no clock in the ward so I don't know what the time is when I wake up.

The nurses are very caring towards me. They come to me when I'm awake and ask me how I feel, and do their best to make me comfortable. I think it's still the same day because every time I wake up I can still see daylight coming in through the windows. Unless I've the whole night without waking and it is now the next day.

I asked if Ma has arrived yet, but she hasn't. It's a long journey from East Ham to here.

Later

When I woke again it was night. The ward was dark except for low lights. I have survived the whole day. The nurses say Ma hasn't arrived yet. I am sure she will come tomorrow. All I have to do is stay alive for the night and get through to the morning. I want to say goodbye to her before I go, and let her know how much I love her and Dad. I want her to tell Dad that I was thinking of both of them as I lay here, that my last thoughts were of them.

Later

Daylight. I have made it through to the new day. Unfortunately, there's a kind of dullness to my eyes and I can't see as clearly as I should. I can see things and people when they're up close, but it's all a bit dim when they are away from me. It feels like there's a weight on my chest the whole time now, and I'm having difficulty breathing. The nurses have given me more medicine for the pain in my legs and chest, but they say they can't do much to help my breathing.

It also seems that everything is muffled, as if my ears are blocked. When I was young I once had wax build up in my ears. Ma cleared it out with warm water. It came out in a lump and then I could hear properly again. I wonder if I've got wax in my ears again? I can't think why I would get wax all of a sudden like this, so maybe it's something else. I wonder if this is dying? I keep hoping to see my ma, but so far she hasn't come.

Still daylight coming in through the windows. Lots of action in the hospital. Nurses hurrying around, patients coughing and choking, and metal basins being put down and picked up, and trolleys being wheeled. At least, I think that's what it is. It's all a bit of a muddle of noise. I try to pick out particular sounds, but they all seem to blur into one whooshing sound that keeps coming and going. I can hear voices and I can sort out men's and women's, but I can't recognize who is talking. I keep thinking I hear my Ma's voice, but the nurses say she hasn't come yet. It's hard to tell who is who around me. My eyes are dimmer now. I can see it's daylight, but I can't see people's faces clearly. I hope my ma comes while I can still see. I would dearly like to see her face before I die.

Later

Sleep again. Wake again. Sleep again. All the noise seems further away now. A nurse came to me and bent over me. I knew it was a nurse because I could smell the starch of her uniform. I hope the same will happen when my ma arrives. I will know her by her smell, and I'll be able to see the outline of her face.

The weight on my chest is really heavy now. It's like it's pushing me down on to the bed. I know I can never sit up. My ma will have to lean right over me for me to see her, but I will know she is here. All I have to do is hang on. She will be here soon, I know.

Later

Someone touched me and I woke up. "Ma?" I said. "Is that you?"

"Not yet," said a woman's voice, and I realized it was a nurse.

I tried to sit up, but the weight on me was too heavy.

"Give Ma my love," I said. "I know she's coming."

Those were Jack Cornwell's last words. He died on June 2 1916. Unfortunately, the telegram informing his mother, Lily Cornwell, of Jack's injuries didn't arrive until too late. By the time she reached Grimsby, Jack was dead.

EPILOGUE

by George Cornwell

Canada, 8th January 1921

Today would have been Jack's 21st birthday, if he'd lived. But he didn't. He died, killed in the Battle of Jutland. Dad also died. Ma died. Arthur died. Me, I'm now living in Canada, and glad to be here.

The war ended just over two years ago in November 1918, when Germany surrendered. The armistice was signed on 11 November. The eleventh hour of the eleventh day of the eleventh month, so that everyone would always remember it as the day the worst war the world had ever known ended.

How do I feel? Relieved that the war ended, and also angry. Not as angry as I was at first, after Jack died. They say time makes things feel better, but it doesn't. All it does is soften things a bit.

Jack died – aged sixteen – on the 2 June 1916. He was part of a gun crew on HMS *Chester*. His ship was hit by four German battlecruisers just minutes after they'd gone into battle. They'd only managed to fire off one salvo when the Germans hit the place where Jack's gun was. All the rest of that gun crew were killed, Jack was the only one who survived. Not that he survived long. He had pieces of metal deep inside his chest and the rest of his body was torn up with shrapnel. But he stayed at his post, by the gun, with the rest of his crew dead all around him. And he didn't just stay at his post, he *stood* at his post. That's what we heard later from the medical orderlies on board who found him. When they reached him, Jack was standing there, with his headphones on, bleeding, but still waiting for orders. That's the sort of person Jack was. Brave. Someone who always did his duty. I wish the people in charge had done their duty by Jack, and the rest of us.

We were told later by the nurses at Grimsby General that Jack kept asking for his ma. He'd been told she was on her way. The truth is that the telegram that was sent to Ma telling her Jack was dying didn't arrive until after he was dead. Whether someone made a mistake, or was lazy and didn't send the telegram as soon as they should have, or just got things wrong, we never found out. As soon as Ma got the telegram telling her Jack was in hospital and not expected to live, she hurried off and caught the train north to Grimsby, determined to see Jack before he died. But when she got there he was already dead.

The navy sent Jack's body home to us for burial. We'd have loved to have given him a proper burial in a churchyard with a headstone and everything. But we were just a poor family from the East End of London. We didn't have any money to bury Jack properly, so he was laid to rest in a communal grave in Manor Park Cemetery, East Ham. A communal grave means that lots of coffins are buried in the same grave. They dig a pit 25 feet [about eight metres] deep and the coffins are placed in one on top of the other. Then the grave's marked with a wooden numbered post rather than any headstone or ceremonial marking. Jack was buried in Communal Grave Number 323.

It was only after Jack had been buried that word began to come out about what had really happened during the Battle of Jutland. I think the government wanted to keep quiet the fact that large numbers of British sailors had died, about 6,000 – and a big number of British ships that had been sunk. But Jutland had been a British victory. The German fleet had been forced back into their own rivers in Germany, and they never came out again. Well, not in the same great numbers.

And word spread about the bravery of the men who'd been involved in the battle. Not just the admirals and the captains, but about the ordinary sailors. And word began to be heard about Jack.

One of the big papers, *The Daily Sketch*, sent a reporter to our house to ask about Jack, and asked where he was buried because they wanted a photograph of his grave for their paper. We showed them the wooden marker post on the communal grave.

Next thing we know, there's a whole article about Jack in the paper, calling him a hero, and saying what a disgrace that he was buried in a "pauper's grave" without even a headstone with his name on it.

Ma was upset about this. She preferred things to be private and didn't like all the world knowing our business, especially the bit about the "pauper's grave". I knew she was worried what Dad would say when he read about that because he didn't like other people knowing our business either.

Me, I told her I was glad the paper was saying it, because I felt it was wrong that Jack hadn't had a decent burial. It wasn't our fault we couldn't afford to bury him in the way he should have been buried. Jack deserved a grave and a headstone fit for a hero.

The paper began its campaign, demanding that the authorities do the decent thing by Jack. Letters from ordinary people came in to the paper, and to the government and the navy, protesting about the fact that Jack was in an unmarked grave. Finally the authorities announced that Jack's coffin was to be exhumed, which meant it was going to be taken out of the communal grave, and reburied in a proper grave with full military honours.

Luckily, Jack's coffin was at the top of the pile of coffins. If his coffin had been at the bottom, it would have been a terrible mess, lifting out all the other coffins on top of him. Bearing in mind what happened much later, my guess is that they wouldn't have bothered. They would have just taken out the top coffin and said that was Jack's anyway. But we'll come to that later.

They opened the grave and took out Jack's coffin, and made a new and better looking coffin around it. Then, on 29 July 1916, Jack was reburied, again in Manor Park Cemetery, but this time with full military honours.

In all my life I have never seen anything like it. It seemed to me like the whole world was there. For a start, the entire route of the funeral procession, from East Ham Town Hall to Manor Park Cemetery, was lined by members of the armed forces, especially sailors, all standing to attention and saluting as Jack's coffin came past them.

The funeral procession left East Ham Town Hall at 3 o'clock in the afternoon. Mounted police officers were right at the front. Behind them came a band from the Royal Navy playing stirring marches, followed by a firing party with their rifles at "slope arms" on their shoulders. Behind the firing party came Jack's new coffin, mounted on a gun carriage and draped over with a Union Jack. Sitting on top of the coffin was Jack's naval cap.

Immediately behind the coffin walked a massive procession of dignitaries, all moving in a slow and sombre way, including the Mayor of East Ham, the Member of Parliament for the local area, the Bishop of Barking and a lot of other churchmen. Behind them came the St Nicholas Boys' School Band, also playing. Behind them was a procession of boys from our old school, Walton Road. Behind all that lot were a load of boy sailors from HMS *Chester*, plus the 2nd Battalion of the Essex Regiment, and also Boy Scout troops, as a mark of Jack's time as a Boy Scout.

I was at the back of all these people, and as the funeral march came past the Alverstone Road area of Manor Park, the rest of our family joined me. Dad had been given compassionate leave to come home for the funeral, and he joined the procession along with Ma, Fred, Lily, Alice, and Ernest. I was glad to see Ernest was there

We all walked along behind this procession to Manor Park Cemetery. There may have been bigger funerals for kings and queens and prime ministers and such, but I never was part of anything so big in my whole life.

When we got to Manor Park the bishop made a speech about sacrifice and Jack being a hero, then they reburied Jack in a newly dug grave, and as his coffin was lowered the firing party let out a volley of shots and the last post was sounded. Then the men who'd been on HMS *Chester*, placed a big floral tribute in the shape of an anchor by Jack's grave.

After that, there were more speeches, most of them on the same theme – sacrifice, doing your duty as Jack had done, all words and sentiments that would have made Jack proud to hear. Then the funeral was over, and we went home, back to our little house in Alverstone Road. And the next day Dad went back to the barracks at Colchester.

That wasn't the end of it, though. The outpouring of grief and pride in Jack from the general public, and not just in London but right across the country – indeed right across the whole British Empire – made the government decide to use Jack to raise morale for the war effort. Jack was going to be an example to all other young men to do their duty and fight for their country. There were demands made in the press and in Parliament for there to be a proper award to honour his bravery, not just the big funeral that had been held in July. So, in the middle of September, Ma got a letter from the government that said:

"The King has been graciously pleased to approve the grant of the Victoria Cross to Boy, First Class, John Travers Cornwell O.N. J. 42563 (died 2 June 1916), for the conspicuous act of bravery specified below:

"Mortally wounded early in the action, Boy, First Class, John Travers Cornwell remained standing alone at a most exposed post, quietly awaiting orders, until the end of the action, with the gun's crew dead and wounded all around him. His age was under sixteen-and-a-half years."

The Victoria Cross! The highest award for bravery! It was the biggest honour the country could have given Jack. Ma was told she would have to go to Buckingham Palace to receive the medal on Jack's behalf from King George V himself. I must admit, I felt a great deal of pride as I helped Ma write the letter to Dad in which she told him about Jack being awarded the VC. I knew it would buck him up. And we both felt Dad would need bucking up, because his last letter to us had been written from a hospital. He'd been taken ill, he said. Nothing serious, just a bit of a cough, and he was being well looked after. He hoped to get back to see us soon, because he was overdue for some leave, and he wanted to visit Jack's grave.

I wrote to Dad, sending him a copy of the letter from the government telling us about Jack being awarded the VC. I got Alice to copy it out because her writing is much neater than mine, and a letter as important as that needed to look proper when Dad read it.

After the story of Jack being awarded the Victoria Cross appeared in the newspapers, the government decided to use this latest news, and Jack's bravery, to raise money from the public. In the same month that Jack's VC was announced, September 1916, the Boy Cornwell Memorial Fund was set up. The aim of this fund was to provide a ward for disabled servicemen at the Star and Garter Home in Richmond. Every schoolchild in the British Empire was encouraged to give a penny towards the fund.

In addition, a local memorial fund in East Ham was set up for Jack's grave. Money was raised from all the schools in the area, and all the local schoolchildren were urged to make donations to the cost of a memorial, as well as other charitable causes.

To help raise money, the governement decided to use a photo of Jack. Their plan was to print this photo of Jack on things like postcards, cigarette cards, beer mats, badges, and all sorts of items, and then sell them. The only problem was, there weren't any photos of Jack. Growing up, there was hardly enough money for important things like paying the rent and buying food and coal, let alone luxuries like paying to have photos of us taken. So they decided to cheat.

A man from one of the government departments – I don't know which one – turned up at our house and asked if I'd like to help our country. I was fifteen at the time, so I wasn't sure how I could help. I was too young to join the army or the navy and – with Jack dead and Dad and Arthur away – it was only my wages that were keeping us.

"They say you look a lot like your brother, Jack," the man said.

"So they say," I replied.

Personally, I didn't think I did look very much like Jack. He was a bit podgier than me about the face, but we were certainly similar.

"Would you let us photograph you?" he asked.

"Why?" I replied, puzzled.

"Because we need a photo of your brother, Jack, but we haven't got one. So what we'd like to do is photograph you, dressed up in a sailor's uniform, and put it out as being Jack."

I stared at him. "But that's a cheat and a lie!" I said.

"No it isn't," he replied. "There aren't any photos of Jack so no-one knows what he looks like, and people want to know. We need a photo to honour him. We need it to make people remember him, and help this country win this war."

Well, when he put it like that, I couldn't really refuse. I knew it was what Jack would have wanted. And, like he said, outside the family, no one would know the photo wasn't really of Jack. So I went along to this photographer's studio, and they gave me a sailor's outfit to put on, complete with a navy hat. I was a bit annoyed that they didn't have a cap with the name of Jack's ship HMS *Chester* on it. Instead, it had HMS *Lancaster* on the tallyband. I pointed this out to the photographer, but he just said "No one will notice". Then I stood with my arms folded and a serious look on my face while he took my photo. Afterwards I changed into my everyday clothes and went home.

Pretty soon that photograph of me was everywhere – in the papers, in magazines, on badges and postcards – with the caption "The hero Jack Cornwell" under it. Everyone in our family and our area knew the truth, but, like the man said, no one else did. So that's the true story of the famous photo of my brother Jack that went all round the world – it isn't Jack, it's me.

After the photo was printed, other people wanted pictures of Jack. Some artist got in touch because the government were paying him to paint Jack standing alone by the gun of the *Chester*, and the government had told him it was actually me in that photo, so he asked if I would pose for him at his studio, wearing the sailor uniform again. I told him I couldn't because I was working and we needed the money. He offered to pay me, but I said that if I took time off, I could get the sack, and I couldn't afford for that to happen. So instead he asked my younger brother, Fred, if he'd pose for him instead.

Fred was as pleased as punch to think that someone wanted to paint a picture of him, even though it was supposed to be of Jack. So Fred posed for the picture and it became famous and was hung in some important gallery, and copies of it were made and sold all over the world.

It was while all this was going on that we got the bad news. Dad died on 25 October 1916. The "cough that's nothing to worry about," as he'd written in his letter, had turned into pneumonia. He died just four months after Jack. In my opinion, Jack being killed took the life out of him.

When his body was returned home, he was buried in the

same grave as Jack, and his name added to the headstone.

Ma was shattered when she got the news about Dad dying. What was worse, with Dad gone, the government stopped his pay, so she had even less money to live on. Me and Alice did our best, but we were struggling to look after ourselves, let alone look after Fred and young Lily. Despite that, on 16 November 1916, Ma went to Buckingham Palace and received the Victoria Cross from King George V on Jack's behalf. She wore her best dress and her best coat for the occasion.

After that, it was back to life as normal in Alverstone Road. Well, not really life as normal. Dad was gone, Jack was gone. Then, in 1918, Arthur was killed in action.

During all this time I supposed that money had been rolling in to the different funds set up in Jack's name. One thing was for sure, we never saw any of it. Ma was the one who suffered most. She got a small pension because of Dad dying, but it wasn't enough to live on. Me and Alice helped her when we could, but it was a struggle for us. By the time the war was over, young Fred was working as well, and he moved away with his work.

Ma took a job at a hostel for sailors to try and make ends meet, but she only got a very small wage, so it wasn't a great deal of help. Finally, desperate, she went to the memorial fund set up in Jack's name and asked for some money. After all, the fund had been set up to help charitable causes, and what was more charitable than to help a woman whose son the fund had been named after and who had lost her husband and another son to the war?

The people who ran the fund said no. They told her she wasn't a worthy cause.

I felt so angry when they said that. These people, none of whom fought in the war, or did anything to help the country except sit behind desks and push pieces of paper around, had the nerve to say no. All the money they had hold of had been raised in the name of Ma's dead son, Jack. He had been her sacrifice. And yet they gave her nothing. They said that the money was to be used to erect a memorial at Jack's grave. Surely, our Ma was Jack's greatest memorial. She'd brought him into this world, she'd hurried to his bedside as soon as she'd been told he was dying.

Finally, Ma couldn't afford to pay the rent on the house at Alverstone Road. Me and Alice had already told her she ought to give it up and move somewhere smaller, because with me also leaving home, the house would be too big for her to manage on her own. In the end she moved into a couple of tiny rooms in Commercial Road in Stepney. There, things went from bad to worse. She cut down on eating to try and save money, and starved. Because I wasn't living at home, I didn't see it happening. Poor Ma was found dead in her rooms on 31 October 1919. She was just 48 years old.

She was buried in the same grave as Jack and Dad at Manor Park Cemetery, but even in death they did her a further injustice. Someone put the wrong name on the headstone. Instead of "Lily, wife of Eli Cornwell and mother of Jack Cornwell, VC" they put "Alice…".

Alice was the name of Dad's first wife. Someone in some office somewhere must have just looked up the records of marriage for Eli Cornwell, seen the name "Alice" and given that name to the stonemason. I went to see the stonemason and told him to remove "Alice" and carve "Lily" instead, but he said he couldn't. He'd been paid to carve that name, and that's what he'd done. He demanded to know who'd pay him to take it off and carve another name on there instead.

That was it for me. I decided that there was nothing left for me in England, and I made up my mind to start a new life in Canada. I've been in Canada for nearly two years now, and I'm glad I made the move. I've been in touch with the others to tell them how I'm doing, and what a great country this is, and Lily says she's planning to come out here too, as soon as she's 18 and can legally move.

I still see that famous photo of me dressed up as Jack, in shops and different places, and every now and then someone comes up and tells me how much I look like Jack Cornwell, the famous boy VC, and I have to smile. I'm tempted to tell them the truth, and a few of my friends know the real story, but mostly I just smile and say, "Yes, I do. But then, I'm his brother." Then I tell them about Jack and what he was like as a boy, and what a hero he was. Because he was. He was brave and he died doing his duty. My brother was a true hero.

One final thing: I read in the papers that last month they finally erected the marble memorial to Jack in East Ham. The story says:

"On 31 December 1920, at a ceremony presided over by Dr Macnamara, MP, representing the Admiralty, the Mayor of East Ham, along with members of the Cornwell family, local Boy Scouts and Sea Scouts as a guard of honour, the memorial to Jack Cornwell was unveiled in his home borough of East Ham, London...

The inscription on the memorial reads: 'In memoriam. First Class Boy JOHN TRAVERS CORNWELL, VC. Born 8 January 1900. Died of wounds received at the Battle of Jutland 2 June 1916. This stone was erected by scholars and ex-scholars of schools in East Ham. 'It is not wealth or ancestry but honourable conduct and a noble disposition that makes man great.' DM"

Historical Note

The Battle of Jutland – which took place in the North Sea off the coast of Denmark, between the British Grand Fleet and the German High Seas Fleet – is considered by many naval historians to be the biggest sea battle since Henry VIII's time. Bigger even than Trafalgar, or the defeat of the Spanish Armada, it was the last great naval battle. All subsequent sea battles were dominated by the addition of aircraft.

Up until 1916 the German fleet, wary of the supposed superiority of the British fleet at the start of the First World War, kept mainly to German waters. The German naval war was mainly conducted by U-boats (German submarines), determined to stop supplies to and from Britain. During the U-boat offensive many civilian liners were attacked and sunk, including the *Lusitania*.

In January 1915 the German fleet launched an attack on the British fleet, but were repulsed at the Battle of Dogger Bank in the North Sea. After this, the German fleet returned to German waters until 24 April 1916, when they launched a surprise attack on the east coast of England, bombarding the towns of Lowestoft and Yarmouth.

The German fleet then withdrew, but were planning a major naval offensive against Britain in late May 1916.

However, a German code book had been captured by British Intelligence, and experts used this code book to decipher messages intercepted over German wireless, and it was realized that Germany was planning a major naval assault on the North Sea coast at the end of May. The British Grand Fleet was ordered into the North Sea to confront the German fleet.

The two opposing fleets were huge. The British Grand Fleet (commanded by Admiral Sir John Jellicoe, with Admiral Sir David Beatty as his second in command) consisted of 28 battleships, 9 battlecruisers, 8 armoured cruisers, 26 light cruisers, 78 destroyers, 1 minelayer and 1 seaplane carrier. The German High Seas Fleet (commanded by Admiral Reinhard Scheer, with Admiral Franz Hipper as his second-in-command) consisted of 16 battleships, 5 battlecruisers, 6 pre-dreadnoughts, 11 light cruisers and 61 torpedo boats.

But the scale of the fleets wasn't just about the number of ships; it was their size and construction. The battleships, especially the dreadnoughts, were unlike anything ever seen before. Huge iron ships, replacing the wooden ships that had sailed the seas for centuries.

On 31 May 1916 Admiral Scheer sent a fleet of

battleships along the Danish coast, hoping to tempt the British fleet out from its harbours. He planned to use U-boats to attack the British ships.

The British commander-in-chief, Admiral Jellicoe, had received information about Scheer's plans from the code-breaking unit of British naval intelligence the day before, 30 May, and decided to engage the German fleet head-on.

Both fleets set sail in the early hours of the morning of 31 May, but they didn't meet up until mid-afternoon, when cruisers from both sides, scouting for sightings of the enemy, spotted the other. After a brief exchange of gunfire, the cruisers alerted their commanders.

At this stage, the Battle of Jutland was noticeable for another "first" – the use of a ship as an aircraft carrier in action. HMS *Engadine* launched a Short 184 seaplane, piloted by Flight Lieutenant Rutland, Assistant Paymaster Trewin as observer. The seaplane flew over the German fleet to assess the size of the enemy and their positions. Because of heavy cloud, the seaplane was forced to fly low at a height of 900 metres, and the German light cruisers fired on the plane with (in the words of Admiral Beatty) "every gun they could bear". The seaplane survived this barrage and was able to return. It reported that the German fleet was indeed a massive force.

On both sides, the giant battlecruisers and the rest

of the fleet were signalled to be brought up into their respective formations, ready for battle.

At 15.48 hours, with both sides about 18,500 metres apart, both fleets opened fire. Firing continued, with the ships doing their best to steer a zig-zag course at the same time to avoid being hit by enemy ordinance. The result of all this gunfire was a haze, which prevented any clear sightings of the enemy, or indeed of the ships in their own fleet.

The British fleet suffered the first major blows: at 16.03 the *Indefatigable* suffered five hits in rapid succession and blew up. At 16.25 the *Queen Mary* received a broadside from the German battlecruiser *Derfflinger*, and the *Queen Mary* blew up and sank within 90 seconds.

At 17.27 the ship on which Jack Cornwell served, HMS *Chester*, was attacked by four German Kaiserliche marine cruisers, each the same size as the *Chester* at close range of 6,000 yards, and it was hit seventeen times by 150mm shells. The *Chester's* armour meant that the interior of the ship suffered little serious damage. On deck, however, the situation was appalling: the casulaties amounted to 29 men killed and 49 wounded. The *Chester's* gun mounting were open-backed shields and did not reach the deck. Because of this, splinters passed beneath the shields or hit the open back when shells exploded nearby, or behind, and many of the wounded lost their legs. The gun mounting where Jack

Cornwell was serving as a sight-setter took at least four hits. It is believed this gun only just managed to get off one salvo before it was hit.

After the action, Jack was found to be the only survivor at his gun. Shards of steel had penetrated his chest; but he had stayed standing at his gun sight and told the sailors who found him he was still awaiting orders.

Before the German cruisers could finish the *Chester* off, the 3rd Battlecruiser Squadron (HMS *Invincible*, HMS Inflexible, and HMS *Indomitable*) came to the aid of the *Chester* and the other British light cruisers that were engaged in the action.

The *Chester* was now effectively out of action, and was forced to return to the port of Immingham.

As the *Chester* journeyed south, the crew members who had died, including those from the crew of Jack's gun, were buried at sea. Usually the ship's chaplain carried out the service, but in this case the *Chester's* chaplain was among the dead, so the funeral oration was read by Captain Lawson. Lawson had himself been wounded in the attack and those who were there said he made an impressive sight, standing at the head of a ladder that led up from the starboard wait of the ship, his head bandaged and his grey beard stained with blood. (As a footnote, Lawson's pet sheepdog, which was on board with him, was also wounded in the attack, but the wound wasn't serious.)

When the *Chester* reached the port of Immingham, Jack Cornwell was transferred to Grimsby General Hospital. He was clearly dying. He died on 2 June 1916.

Off the Danish coast, the battle at sea raged for some hours more, with both sides hampered by the thick haze from gunsmoke, combined with the blinding light from the setting sun. The British fleet were also troubled with problems caused by poor signalling.

At 18.30 hours the German fleet headed back towards the German coast. Initially, Jellicoe was reluctant to send the British fleet in pursuit, fearing there could be traps ahead of minefields, and especially ambushes by German submarines. However, the German fleet then separated and doubled back, apparently attempting to get around to the rear of the British line. The sea battle then resumed, with as full force as before.

As night fell the battle continued, with more ships being sunk. Action continued throughout the night into the early hours of the following morning (1 June). The final casualty of the battle was the German dreadnought *Ostfriesland*, which was severely damaged by a British mine as it approached the Jade River at 05.30 hours on 1 June.

The final casualties, both in shipping and men, were as massive as the two respective fleets. The British fleet suffered 6,094 men killed, 510 wounded, and 177 captured; the German fleet lost 2,551 killed with 507 wounded. The

British fleet lost 3 battlecruisers, 3 armoured cruisers and 8 destroyers. The German fleet lost 1 pre-dreadnought, 1 battlecruiser, 4 light cruisers and 5 torpedo boats. The total tonnage sunk for the British Fleet was 113,300 tons and the German Fleet, 62,300 tons.

Afterwards the British government did their best to hush up the British losses in the Battle of Jutland. Officers and men who had taken part in the battle were ordered not to mention it, but the Admiralty were forced to issue a press statement in which they grudgingly admitted that there had been a "naval engagement" off the Jutland coast. Why the secrecy? Because the British losses, both in ships and men, had been so high that the government were worried that it would be seen as a failure. The losses of the huge battlecruisers *Queen Mary*, *Invincible* and *Indefatigable*, all destroyed with all hands. 3,000 men dead in those three sinkings, with another 3,000 British dead among the rest of the British fleet.

But the Battle of Jutland marked the demise of the German fleet. Defeated at Jutland, the German fleet retreated to German waters, and remained there until the end of the First World War.

The father of Queen Elizabeth II, then known as Sub-Lieutenant Prince Albert, later King George VI, fought in the battle as a sub-lieutenant on board the *Collingwood*.

The ships of the two opposing navies in action at the Battle of Jutland:

Grand Fleet of the British Royal Navy:
2nd Battle Squadron:

1st Division: *King George V* (Capt. Field Vice Admiral Jerram); *Ajax* (Capt. Baird); *Centurion* (Capt. Culme-Seymour); *Erin* (Capt. Stanley).

2nd Division: *Orion* (Capt. Backhouse; Rear Admiral Leveson); *Monarch* (Capt. Borrett); *Conqueror* (Capt. Tothill); *Thunderer* (Capt. Fergusson).

4th Battle Squadron:

3rd Division: *Iron Duke* (Capt. Dreyer; Admiral Jellicoe); *Royal Oak* (Capt. MacLachlan); *Superb* (Capt. Hyde-Parker; Rear Admiral Duff); *Canada* (Capt. Nicholson).

4th Division: *Benbow* (Capt. Parker; Vice Admiral Sturdee); *Bellerophon*; *Temeraire* (Capt. Underhill); *Vanguard* (Capt. Dick).

1st Battle Squadron:

5th Division: *Colossus* (Capt. Pound; Rear Admiral Gaunt); *Collingwood* (Capt. Ley); *Neptune* (Capt. Bernard); *StVincent* (Capt. Fisher).

6th Division: *Marlborough* (Capt. Ross; Vice-Admiral Burney); *Revenge* (Capt. Kiddle); *Hercules* (Capt. Bernard); *Agincourt* (Capt. Doughty).

3rd Battlecruiser Squadron: *Invincible* (Capt. Cay; Rear-Admiral Hood); *Inflexible* (Capt. Heaton-Ellis); *Indomitable* (Capt. Kennedy).

Armored Cruisers:

1st Cruiser Squadron: Defence (Capt. Ellis; Rear-Admiral Arbuthnot); *Warrior* (Capt. Molteno); *Duke of Edinburgh* (Capt. Blackett); *Black Prince* (Capt. Bonham).

2nd Cruiser Squadron: *Minotaur* (Capt. d'Aeth; Rear-Admiral Heath); *Hampshire* (Capt. Savill); *Cochrane* (Capt. Leatham); *Shannon* (Capt. Dumaresq).

4th Light Cruiser Squadron: *Calliope* (Commodore Le Mesurier); *Constance* (Capt. Townsend); *Caroline* (Capt. Crooke); *Royalist* (Capt. Meade); *Comus* (Capt. Hotham).

Attached Light Cruisers

Active (Capt. Withers); *Bellona* (Capt. Dutton); *Blanche* (Capt. Casement); *Boadicea* (Capt. Casement); *Canterbury* (Capt. Royds); *Chester* (Capt. Lawson).

Destroyers:

4th Flotilla: *Tipperary* (Capt. Wintour); *Acasta*; *Achates*; *Ambuscade*; *Ardent*; *Broke*; *Christopher*; *Contest*; *Fortune*; *Garland*; *Hardy*; *Midge*; *Ophelia*; *Owl*; *Porpoise*; *Shark*; *Sparrowhawk*; *Spitfire*; *Unity*.

11th Flotilla: *Castor* (Commodore Hawksley); *Kempenfelt*; *Magic*; *Mandate*; *Manners*; *Marne*; *Martial*; *Michael*; *Millbrook*; *Minion*; *Mons*; *Moon*; *Morning Star*; *Mounsey*; *Mystic*; *Ossory*.

12th Flotilla: *Faulknor* (Capt. Stirling); *Maenad*; *Marksman*; *Marvel*; *Mary Rose*; *Menace*; *Mindful*; *Mischief*; *Munster*; *Narwhal*; *Nessus*; *Noble*; *Nonsuch*; *Obedient*; *Onslaught*; *Opal*.

Minelayer: *Abdiel*.

Oak: tender to HMS Iron Duke

Seaplane carrier: *Engadine*.

The Battlecruiser Fleet:

1st Battlecruiser squadron: *Lion* (Capt. Chatfield; Vice-Admiral Beatty); *Princess Royal* (Capt. Cowan; Rear-Admiral de Brock); *Queen Mary* (Capt. Prowse); *Tiger* (Capt. Pelly).

2nd Battlecruiser Squadron: *New Zealand* (Capt. Green; Rear-Admiral Pakenham); *Indefatigable* (Capt. Sowerby).

5th Battle Squadron: *Barham* (Capt. Craig; Rear-Admiral Evan-Thomas); *Valiant* (Capt. Woollcombe); *Warspite* (Capt. Philpotts); *Malaya* (Capt. Boyle).

1st Light Cruiser: Squadron: *Galatea* (Commodore Alexander-Sinclair); *Phaeton* (Capt. Cameron); *Inconstant* (Capt. Thesiger); *Cordelia* (Capt. Beamish).

2nd Light Cruiser Squadron: *Southampton* (Commodore Goodenough); *Birmingham* (Capt. Duff); *Nottingham* (Capt. Miller); *Dublin* (Capt. Scott).

3rd Light Cruiser Squadron: *Falmouth* (Capt. Edwards; Rear-Admiral Napier); *Yarmouth* (Capt. Pratt); *Birkenhead* (Capt. Reeves); *Gloucester* (Capt. Blunt).

1st Destroyer Flotilla: *Fearless* (Capt. Roper); *Acheron*; *Ariel*; *Attack*; *Badger*; *Defender*; *Goshawk*; *Hydra*; *Lapwing*; *Lizard*.

9th and 10th Destroyer Flotillas (combined): *Lydiard* (Commander Goldsmith); *Landrail*; *Laurel*; *Liberty*; *Moorsom*; *Morris*; *Termagant*; *Turbulent*.

13th Destroyer Flotilla: *Champion* (Capt. Farie); *Moresby*; *Narborough*; *Nerisaa*; *Nestor*; *Nicator*; *Nomad*; *Obdurate*; *Onslow*; *Pelican*; *Petard*.

High Seas Fleet of the Imperial German Navy:
III Battle Squadron:
5th Division: *Konig* (Capt. Bruninghaus; Rear-Admiral Behncke); *Grosser Kurfurst* (Capt. Goette); *Kronprinz* (Capt. Feldt); *Markgraf* (Capt. Seiferling).

6th Division: *Kaiser* (Capt. von Keyserlingk; Rear-Admiral Nordmann); *Kaiserin* (Capt. Sievers); *Prinzregent Luitpold* (Capt. Heuser); *Friedrich der Grosse* (Capt. Fuchs; Vice-Admiral Scheer).

1st Battle Squadron:
1st Division: *Ostfriesland* (Capt. von Natzmer; Vice-Admiral Schmidt); *Thuringen* (Capt. Kusel); *Helgoland* (Capt. von Kameke); *Oldenburg* (Capt. Redlich).

2nd Division: *Posen* (Capt. Lange; Rear-Admiral Engelhardt); *Rheinland* (Capt. Rohardt); *Nassau* (Capt. Klappenbach); *Westfalen* (Capt. Redlich).

III Battle Squadron:

3rd Division: *Deutschland* (Capt. Meurer; Rear-Admiral Mauve); *Hessen* (Capt. Bartels); *Pommern* (Capt. Bolken).

4th Division: *Hannover* (Capt. Heine; Rear-Admiral von Dalwigk zu Lichtenfels); *Schlesien* (Capt. Behncke); *Schleswig-Holstein* (Capt. Barrentrapp).

Light Cruisers:

IV Scouting Group: *Stettin* (Capt. Rebensburg; Commodore von Reuter); *Munchen* (Capt. Bocker); *Hamburg* (Capt. von Gaudecker); *Frauenlob* (Capt. Hoffmann); *Stuttgart* (Capt. Hagedorn).

Torpedo-Boat Flotillas

Light Cruiser Torpedo Boat: Rostock (Capt. Feldmann; Commodore Michelson).

Torpedo-Boat Flotilla: *G39* (Commander Albrecht); *G40*; *G38*; *S32*.

III Torpedo-Boat Flotilla: *S53* (Commander Hollmann); *V71*; *V73*; *G88*; *S54*; *V48*; *G42*.

V Torpedo-Boat Flotilla: *G11* (Commander Heinecke); *V1*; *V2*; *V3*; *V4*; *V5*; *V6*; *V7*; *G7*; *G8*; *G9*; *G10*.

VII Torpedo-Boat Flotilla: *S24* (Commander von Koch); *S15*; *S16*; *S17*; *S18*; *S19*; *S20*; *S23*; *V186*; *V189*.

The Battlecruiser Force:

I Scouting Group (Battlecruisers): Lutzow (Capt. Harder; Vice-Admiral Hipper); *Derfflinger* (Capt. Hartog); *Seydlitz* (Capt. von Egidy); *Moltke* (Capt. von Karpf); *Von der Tann*

(Capt. Zenker).

II Scouting Group (Light Cruisers): *Frankfurt* (Capt. von Trotha; Rear-Admiral Bodicker); *Wiesbaden* (Capt. Reiss); *Pillau* (Capt. Mommsen); *Elbing* (Capt. Madlung).

Light Cruiser Boats:

Regensburg (Capt. Heuberer; Commodore Henrich)

II Torpedo-Boat Flotilla: B98 (Capt. Schuur); G1010; G102; G103; G104; B97; B109; B110; B111; B112.

VI Torpedo-Boat Flotilla: G41 (Commander Schultz); V44; V45; V46; V69; G37; G86; G87; S50.

IX Torpedo-Boat Flotilla: V28 (Commander Goehle); V26; V27; V29; V30; S33; S34; S35; S36; S51; S52.

HMS *Chester*

HMS *Chester* was built at the Cammell Laird shipyard in Birkenhead, and was a town-class light cruiser. It was launched in December 1915. It had a displacement of 5,185 tons. It was 456 and a half feet long and 50 feet wide, with a draught of fifteen and a half feet. The engines that drove it were Parsons reaction steam turbines, with twelve Yarrow oil boilers.

It had four propellers, giving it 31,000 horsepower, which meant it could travel at 26 knots, which meant 26 nautical miles an hour. It carried 1,172 tons of fuel oil to power the boilers.

The armour plating of the hull was two inches thick,

and on the actual deck the armour was one-and-a-half inches thick. On the conning tower the steel armour was four inches thick.

The *Chester* had ten five-and-a-half-inch Mark 1 guns made by the Coventry Ordnance Works. They fired an 85-pound shell. This meant the ship had a higher firing rate than a ship with six-inch guns, which fired a 100-pound shell and were slower to reload. The five-and-a-half-inch guns were rare in ships of the Royal Navy. In fact the Chester was only one of two ships in the navy with this size of gun. The reason for this is that the *Chester* and the other ship were originally being built for the Greek navy, and the Greek navy wanted ships with smaller guns because they would be lighter and meant the ships would be faster in the water. But when war was declared the British government commandeered both of those ships for the Royal Navy.

Jack Cornwell and the Boy Scouts.

Jack's membership of the Boy Scouts was very important to him, and his strong association with them can be seen in the fact that the Scouts provided the guard of honour at both Jack's funeral, and at the commemoration of the memorial to him.

After Jack's death the Cornwell Award was created, which was also known as the Scout VC. This is a badge of courage awarded for acts of special bravery to Scouts. The bronze badge is in the shape of the letter "C" encircling the fleur-de-lys, the symbol of the Scouting Movement. The "C" stands for both Cornwell and Courage.

The Canadian Connection.

Jack's brother, George, emigrated to Canada shortly after the end of the First World War. Their sister, Lily, joined George in Canada in 1923 when she was eighteen. A further Canadian connection was made when one of the highest mountains on the border between Alberta and British Columbia was named Mount Cornwell in Jack's honour by the Geographic Board of Canada.

Silvertown Munitions Works

The munitions factory at Silvertown, West Ham, blew up on Friday 19 January 1917, killing 73 people and laying waste to a huge area surrounding the explosion.

The munitions factory was set up in September 1915 at an existing empty factory to produce the explosive TNT for the war effort. Concerns were expressed because TNT was produced and stored in the same building, which many thought was dangerous. Dr F. A. Freeth, who was chief chemist for Brunner Mond, the parent firm that owned the factory, wrote reports to the Ministry of Defence expressing his concerns about the safety of the plant. He later stated that "At the end of every month we used to write to Silvertown to say that their plant would go up sooner or later, and we were told that it was worth the risk to get the TNT".

At 6.52pm on Friday 19th January 1917 a fire in the melting-pot room led to 50 tons of TNT exploding. The blast was heard as far away as Guildford and Cambridge. Around 70,000 in the surrounding area were damaged by the blast. Sixty-nine people were killed in the immediate explosion and another four died later. Four hundred people were injured.

Appendices:

The last letter Jack wrote to his father, Eli Cornwell, just before the Battle of Jutland:

Dear Dad

Just a few lines in answer to your most welcome letter, which we received on Monday – first post for a week. That is why you have not had a letter for a long while. Thanks for the stamps you sent me. We are up in the (CENSORED) somewhere, and they have just put me up as a sight setter at a gun.

Dear Dad, I have just had to start in pencil, as I have run out of ink, but still, I suppose you don't mind as long as you get a letter, and I am sorry to tell you that poor old A.L. is dead, and I dare say by the time you get this letter she will be buried. I have got a lot of letters to send home and about, so I can't afford much more, and we are just about to close up at the gun, so this is all for now: have more next time.

I remain, your ever-loving son,

Jack.

PS – "Cheer up, Buller me lad, we're not dead yet!"

Part of a letter that was written by the captain of HMS *Chester*, Captain Lawson, to Jack's mother after the Battle of Jutland:

Dear Mrs Cornwell

I know you would wish to hear of the splendid fortitude shown by your boy during the action of May 31. His devotion to duty was an example for all of us. The wounds which resulted in his death within a short time were received in the first few minutes of the action. He remained steady at his most exposed post at the gun, waiting for orders.

His gun would not bear on the enemy, all but two of the ten of the crew were killed or wounded, and he was the only one who was in such an exposed position. But he felt he might be needed – as indeed he might have – so he stayed there, standing and waiting, under heavy fire, with just his own brave heart and God's help to support him. I cannot express to you my admiration of the son you have lost from this world. No other comfort would I attempt to give to the mother of so brave a lad, but to assure her of what he was and what he did, and what an example he gave. I hope to place in the boys' mess a plate with his name on and the date, and the words "Faithful unto death". I hope some day you may be able to come and see it there.

Author's acknowledgements

I would like to give my special thanks to Martin Garnett, Curator at the Imperial War Museum, London (whose special responsibility is the famous "Jack Cornwell gun" from HMS *Chester*), for giving up his time to talk me through the gun, its history, and workings; and to Andy Curran and the crew of HMS *Belfast*, with special thanks to Yeoman Lee Harrison, who also spent valuable time showing me through the gun drills and operation of these giant guns. Also, to Terry Charman of the Imperial War Museum, whose expert comments on the text and the period led me to correct quite a few errors in my first draft. Any errors left are my own.

**Other First World War books by Jim
Eldridge, published by Scholastic:**

My Story: The Trenches
(the war in the trenches of the Somme, seen through
the eyes of a young wireless operator)

My Story: Flying Ace
(the war in the air, seen through the eyes of
a young fighter pilot)

Recommended reading:

For those who want to find out more details about the Battle of Jutland, I can recommend the following books:

Andrew Gordon: *The Rules of the Game* (*Jutland and British Naval Command*) (published by John Murray – 1996)

Julian Thompson: *The Imperial War Museum Book of the War at Sea 1914-1918* (published by Sidgwick & Jackson in association with the Imperial War Museum – 2005)

Richard Hallam: "Scrimgeour's Small Scribbling Diary" (published by Conway Maritime -2008). This is the diary of a young naval officer who died when HMS *Invincible* was sunk during the Battle of Jutland.